New Junior Cycle Common Level Science

G000129107

Contents

Student Study Essentials

Topic by Topic Analysis Chart...iii

Guide to Better Grades v

Map Your Progress! viii

Online Study Hub – visit **www.edco.ie/onlinestudyhub**

Completed
(✓)

2023 State Examinations Commission Paper............... (visit www.e-xamit.ie) ....1 ☐

2022 State Examinations Commission Paper............... (visit www.e-xamit.ie) ....29 ☐

2019 State Examinations Commission Paper............... (visit www.e-xamit.ie) ....57 ☐

October 2018 State Examinations Commission
Sample Paper .... (visit www.e-xamit.ie) ....85 ☐

Edco Sample Paper A .... (visit www.e-xamit.ie) ......113 ☐

Edco Sample Paper B ....137 ☐

Edco Sample Paper C ....163 ☐

Edco Sample Paper D ....189 ☐

Edco Sample Paper E ....214 ☐

Edco Sample Paper F..239 ☐

Edco Sample Paper G ....266 ☐

Please note: There was no exam in 2021 and 2020 for Junior Cycle Science.

FREE ONLINE SOLUTIONS
Visit www.e-xamit.ie to access Free Online Tutorials
with Sample Answers, Hints and Tips! (See codes inside.)

Welcome to the new Science at Junior Cycle

Learning Outcome Analysis Chart:

TOPIC	Learning outcome 2023	SEC exam 2023	Learning outcome 2022	SEC exam 2022	Learning outcome 2019	SEC exam 2019	SEC sample	Edco A	Edco B	Edco C	Edco D	Edco E
Nature of science	1.1, 1.2, 1.3, 1.4, 1.5, 1.8, 1.9,	Q7, Q10, Q11, Q12, Q13, Q14	1,1, 1.2, 1.3, 1.4, 1.5, 1.8	Q2, Q3, Q4, Q5, Q6, Q7, Q8, Q9, Q11, Q12, Q13, Q14, Q15	1.2, 1.3, 1.4, 1.5, 1.7, 1.8, 1.9	Q11 Q12 Q13 Q14 Q16	Q10 Q15	Q8 Q11 Q15	Q12, Q14, Q14	Q6	Q12, Q13, Q14, Q15, Q16	Q12, Q13, Q14, Q15, Q16
Animal and plant cell	5.1	Q1			5.1	Q1	Q1				Q4	Q3
Mass, area, volume & density			4.1	Q1	4.2	Q2		Q12	Q8	Q8	Q13	
Force, weight, work	4.1, 4.2	Q14	4.2	Q15	4.2						Q1	
Potential difference, current, voltage, power					4.2							Q10
Water and carbon cycle					2.5	Q3	Q5			Q7		
Conservation of mass and chemical change			3.5	Q3	3.1, 3.2	Q4	Q4		Q2			
Energy & energy conservation	4.8, 4.6	Q10, Q12	4.6, 4.2	Q15	2.8, 4.2, 4.6, 3.4, 4.7		Q13		Q13		Q5	Q11
Inheritance					5.2, 5.4, 5.6	Q5						Q2, Q7
Habitat study	5.5	Q6			5.5, 5.6, 5.7		Q14		Q7			
Ecological biodiversity	5.9	Q6	5.3	Q4	5.10				Q9			
Evolution			5.3	Q4	5.3							
Photosynthesis	5.7	Q11			5.7				Q7		Q12	
Respiration	5.7	Q11, Q14			5.7							Q13
Acid+base	3.8	Q8	3.8	Q9	3.8, 3.9	Q6	Q11		Q11	Q1	Q14	Q12
Energy diagrams	3.9	Q3			3.9	Q6	Q12					
Speed, velocity, acceleration	4.2	Q7	4.2	Q7	4.2	Q7		Q9	Q8	Q10	Q4	
Climate change	2.7	Q11	2.7	Q14	2.7	Q8					Q8	Q9, Q16
Digestive, circulatory & respiratory system	5.4	Q15	5.4	Q10, Q14	5.4	Q9	Q4	Q1	Q5, Q12	Q11	Q10, Q15	
Human health issues	5.6	Q15	5.6	Q14	5.6						Q3	
Galaxies, stars, solar system					2.1, 2.4	Q10		Q10	Q1, Q3			
Celestial objects			2.3, 2.4	Q2	2.1, 2.4	Q10		Q14	Q6	Q3		Q6
Big bang			2.2	Q8								
Eclipses					2.4		Q13					
Comparing planetary data			2.3	Q2	2.1, 2.2, 2.3		Q16	Q3		Q12	Q2	
Space technology & space travel hazards	2.8	Q13	2.8	Q8	2.8				Q15			
Solubility, separating mixtures			3.6	Q5	3.6	Q11	Q3	Q13			Q5	

TOPIC	Learning outcome 2023	SEC exam 2023	Learning outcome 2022	SEC exam 2022	Learning outcome 2019	SEC exam 2019	SEC sample	Edco A	Edco B	Edco C	Edco D	Edco E
Common gas & biochemical reactions	3.7	Q15			3.7		Q15					Q14
Periodic table	3.5	Q9	3.5	Q3	3.5				Q4			Q3
Science equipment & units of measurement			4.1	Q1	4.1			Q5	Q10			
Electronics					4.5	Q12		Q5				
Electricity					4.2, 4.6	Q13	Q9			Q13, Q14	Q9, Q16	Q1
Physical observables	4.3	Q5, Q14			4.3, 4.7					Q14		
Generation & consumption of electricity					4.8					Q9		Q8, Q9
Media based arguments					1.8	Q14		Q8				
Classification of substances	3.2, 3.5	Q4, Q9			3.2, 3.4, 3.5, 3.3	Q15	Q6, Q8	Q2, Q6		Q5, Q13	Q6	Q5
Extraction, disposal & recycling of materials					3.10					Q15		
Plastics					3.6						Q7	
Earth, sun, moon system	2.1	Q13	2.4	Q11	2.1, 2.4	Q16					Q11	Q4
Force, mass, weight					2.3	Q16						
Instruments of measurement	4.1	Q5	4.1	Q1	4.1		Q2					
Reproduction & Inheritance	5.9	Q2	5.2	Q12	5.9		Q7			Q2		
Medical, ethical & societal issues					5.9						Q3	
Atomic structure	3.2, 3.3	Q10	3.2	Q3								
The moon and lunar phases	2.3, 2.4	Q13	2.4, 2.3	Q6								
Titration			3.8	Q9								
Metals and non metals			3.6, 3.2	Q13								
Food	5.6	Q14	5.6	Q14								

Welcome to the new Science at Junior Cycle
Guide to Better Grades

In revising for the Junior Cycle, it is important to keep in mind the following:

i)   The structure of the examination paper

ii)   The way the paper is marked

iii) Understanding the content of each of the five strands of the new curriculum:

  Strand 1 – Nature of Science

  Strand 2 – Earth & Space

  Strand 3 – Chemical World

  Strand 4 – Physical World

  Strand 5 – Biological World

iv)   The language used in the question and paying attention to what you are being asked to explain, interpret etc.

Structure of the Examination Paper

There are two sections to the examination paper

Section A	10 questions	15 marks each	150 marks	Total section A 150 marks
Section B	5 questions	2 questions – Q11&12 carrying 30 marks each	Total 60 marks	Total section B 210 marks
		2 questions – Q13&14 carrying 45 marks each	Total 90 marks	
		1 question carrying 60 marks	Total 60 marks	

The layout of Section A and Section B are based on exam papers and the Sample Paper as issued by the State Examinations Commission.

The new Science paper is a Common Level paper and the allotted timeframe to complete the paper is 2 hours.

Section A

Questions 1 to 10

- As this is a common level paper, all questions in this section MUST be answered.

- You should spend about 50 minutes on Section A.

- All of the answers to these questions have to be written on the examination paper.

- This section carries 42% of the overall marks of the paper, so your time should be spent on making sure that you read all of the questions correctly and answer the question with the relevant information.

- There are 15 marks allocated to each question and this will be indicated on the top of each question in this section. This will result in a total of 150 marks for this section.

- Diagrams and graphs may need to be drawn as part of the question. Take due care to draw the diagrams/graphs correctly and label accordingly.

- This section will contain a combination of all five strands of the new Science specification.

- There is a wide variety of question formats within this question, which will allow for each student to achieve the highest possible opportunity to achieve the highest attainment of marks. See 'question format' for style of questions being asked.

- There is no set pattern in this section and this section will require the student to present information, from the content that they have learned and understood.

- There are no direct definitions asked of the student in this section. Students MUST have a good understanding of the content that they have learned over the three years.

Section B

Section B carries a total marks allocation of 210 marks which will account for 58% of the total marks.

Question 11 to 15

- There are five questions in this section – 2 questions will carry a marks total of 30 marks each and 2 will carry a marks total of 45 marks each and 1 question will carry a marks total of 60 marks. This will total 210 marks for section B.

- This current layout for section B is based on the Exam Paper as issued by the SEC, for the Junior Cycle Science Exam, in June 2022 and 2023.

Questions 11 and 12

- These two questions carry 30 marks each and the questions are based on the 5 strands of the new Science specification.

- There is no set pattern of questions being asked.

- Section B questions will require students to present data, graphs and answers based on their interpretation of the questions.

- There should be no direct definitions asked in this section. Questions will be based on the student's understanding of the contents and skills that they have learned over the three years.

- The content of the questions is based on information and skills that have been acquired and understood over the three years.

Questions 13 and 14

- These two questions carry 45 marks each.

- The content of these questions, based on the Sample Paper and the three examination papers of 2019, 2022 & 2023 issued by the SEC, are analysis-style questions. They will have Science content and will have links to the 5 strands. However, students may not have met the information directly within their learning:

  For example, a question is asked on the Sample Paper based on the moons of Jupiter. This content is not directly within the Earth and Space strand. However, the content of the question was based on students interpreting data from tables and answering the following questions on that data. Students WILL have practiced this skill during their three years of learning.

Questions 15

- This question is a 60 mark question and first appeared on the 2022 examination paper

- The questions asked in 2022 & 2023 required students to interpret information using prior knowledge of the five strands. This long question cross links strands in the Specification and assesses both learning and critical thinking.

Varying style of questions that may be asked

Both Section A and Section B questions will contain a varying style of question formatting. Here are some of the varying styles that may be used:

- 'Fill in the blanks' – a list of words to complete, will be given in the question. Read the text first. A good tip is to fill in the

blanks with a pencil to ensure you get it right. Once you are happy that you have it correct, write over the pencil in biro.

- Multiple choice. Ensure that you read the answers carefully in multiple choice. Some answers in the selection may try to catch you out. So take your time.

- Comprehensions, with questions based on the comprehension paragraph/article following the text. Most of the answers in a comprehension question are found within the text. Ensure you read the text carefully.

- Interpreting tables of data. Hopefully you will have practised interpreting data in your sample papers and textbook. A good tip for making sure you are on the correct part of the table is to place your finger on the table and the part that you are being questioned on. This will focus the eye onto that correction section. And always read your question carefully to see what part of the table you are being asked about.

- Interpreting graphs. Take your time when interpreting graphs. A good tip is to use your pencil to draw a line on the graph following the relevant data that you are being asked about.

- Filling in spaces in tables of data. This is very similar to interpreting data on tables. Be careful that you are filling in

the correct part with the correct answer. Always make sure to check your answers.

- Drawing diagrams. Use a dark pencil when drawing your diagrams, it will make them much easier to see and correct. Make your diagrams big, and draw a straight line, with an arrow, to the exact part you want to label.

- Interpreting data from diagrams. Read your question carefully. What part of the diagram is it asking you to interpret? Ensure you are always answering your question to the relevant part on the diagram.

- Matching up phrases to the correct word. A good tip here is to use your pencil when matching the words. Draw a line from the phrase to the word. If you make an error a pencil is very easy to erase. Use a dark pencil as it is much easier to see.

- Circle the correct answer(s). Read the question carefully. Take your time, ensure you are circling the correct answer.

- Comparison of data/pictures. With all comparisons – data to pictures – take care to ensure that you are comparing the correct picture to the correct piece of data.

This is not an exhaustive list. Ensure that you have practised all of these question styles before you complete your exam.

Be aware of common exam pitfalls.

- These include:
  1. Not reading the paper correctly.
  2. Not finishing the paper.
  3. Handing up the exam paper to the Superintendent without having re-read your answers or having made any corrections or tweaks to the answers that you have given.

Top tips for a great exam

Pay attention to the marking scheme.

- Missing part of a question: when checking your work at the end of the exam, make sure that you have done all the parts specified in each question.

- When you receive your exam paper, spend a few minutes examining the content of the various questions and decide fairly quickly which ones you can do best. Answer those questions first.

- Do not waste too much time trying to think of answers to a particular part of a question. Leave spaces and come back to these later.

- You may find that you will have completed all of the questions before the time allowed. You should then carefully check all of your answers.

- It is very important to show the starting point and the various stages in every calculation so that the examiner can follow what you are doing. If you then make a small mathematical slip and end up with the wrong answer you will not lose all of the marks. If you do not show the starting point and the various stages, and end up with the wrong answer, you may score no marks for that part.

- Pay attention to wording of the questions that you are asked and answer them accordingly based on what you are being asked to do – Example: Explain, Describe, Identify, Outline. You should do this by practising exam style questions before you sit the exam.

Map Your Progress!

Tick each paper as you complete it and tick the sections of the papers as you complete them.

JUNIOR CYCLE SCIENCE PAPER	2023	2022	2019	SEC Sample Paper	Edco Sample A	Edco Sample B	Edco Sample C	Edco Sample D	Edco Sample E	Edco Sample F	Edco Sample G
Section A Questions											
Q1											
Q2											
Q3											
Q4											
Q5											
Q6											
Q7											
Q8											
Q9											
Q10											
Section B – 30 mark questions											
Q11											
Q12											
Q13											
Q14											

JUNIOR CYCLE SCIENCE PAPER	2023	2022	2019	SEC Sample Paper	Edco Sample A	Edco Sample B	Edco Sample C	Edco Sample D	Edco Sample E	Edco Sample F	Edco Sample G
Section B – 45 mark questions											
Q15										Q15	

Junior Cert Grades Chart

Percentage	Grade Descriptor
90 to 100	Distinction
75 and 90	Higher Merit
55 and 75	Merit
40 and 55	Achieved
20 and 40	Partially Achieved
0 and 20	Not Graded (NG)

Study Hub

Your free online guide to smarter study.

Visit

www.edco.ie/onlinestudyhub

Remember

When completing the exam

- Section A questions are a combination of Physical World, Chemical World, Biological World and Earth and Space. These questions should require a shorter length of time to complete.

- Section B questions are also a combination of Physical World, Chemical World, Biological World and Earth and Space.

- There are three types of questions here: 30 marks, 45 marks and 60 mark questions.

- The 30 marks questions will be based on the Learning Outcomes from your curriculum. They will require more time to be spent completing them.

- The 45 mark and 60 mark questions are based on your understanding of the content and the Learning Outcomes. They will require you think about what is being asked of you in the question and how you intend to phrase your answer.

Map Your Progress!

Coimisiún na Scrúduithe Stáit
State Examinations Commission

Junior Cycle Final Examination 2023

Science

Common Level

Monday 12 June   Morning 9:30 – 11:30

360 marks

Examination Number

Day and Month of Birth

For example, 3rd February is entered as 0302

Centre Stamp

Instructions

Write your Examination Number and your Day and Month of Birth in the boxes on the front cover.

There are two sections in this examination paper.

Section A	150 marks	10 questions
Section B	210 marks	5 questions

Answer **all** parts of **all** questions.

You may ask the superintendent for a copy of the *Formulae and Tables* booklet. You must return it at the end of the examination. You are not allowed to bring your own copy into the examination.

Not all the questions carry equal marks. The number of marks for each question is stated at the top of the question.

Write your answers in the spaces provided in this booklet. You are not required to use all of the space provided. There is extra space at the end of Section A and at the back of the booklet. Label any extra work clearly with the question number and part.

This examination booklet will be scanned and your work will be presented to an examiner on screen. Anything that you write outside of the answer areas may not be seen by the examiner.

Write your answers in blue or black pen. You may use pencil for graphs and diagrams only.

Section A   **150 marks**

Question 1   **(15 marks)**

The pictures below show cells from an onion (plant cells) and from the human cheek (animal cells).

Onion (plant cells)   **Human cheek (animal cells)**

   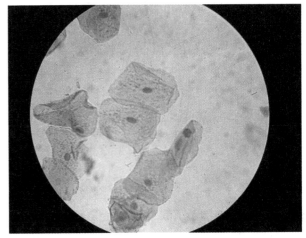

                    N   **N**

(a) For each picture, draw an arrow from the letter **N** written below the picture to the nucleus of a cell.

(b) The names of some of the other parts of cells are listed below.

            Cytoplasm   **Cell membrane**   **Cell wall**

Use the words in the list to complete the table to name each cell part described.

Description of cell part	Name
Controls the movement of substances in and out of cells	
Found in plant cells only	
All of the material inside a cell, except for the nucleus	

3

Question 2   **(15 marks)**

The diagrams below show the reproductive systems for the human female and the human male.

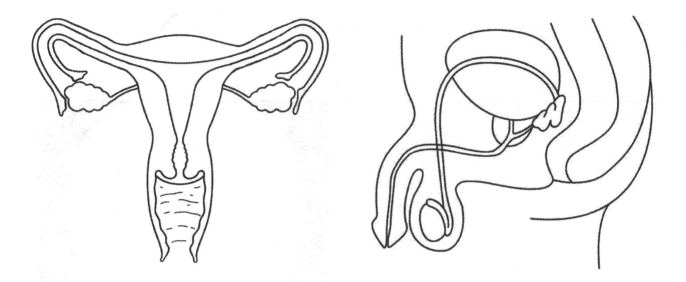

(a)   Use the letter **A** to label the part of the reproductive systems where the female sex cell (egg) is produced.

(b)   Use the letter **B** to label the part of the reproductive systems where the male sex cell (sperm) is produced.

(c)   Use the letter **C** to label the part of the reproductive systems where fertilisation usually occurs.

(d)   Use the letter **D** to label the part of the reproductive systems where the foetus develops during pregnancy.

(e)   Contraception reduces the chance of pregnancy.
           Describe one method of contraception.

Question 3

(a) The diagram below is an energy profile diagram for an exothermic reaction.
Use the words in the list below to label this diagram by filling in the boxes.

Products   **Reactants**   **Energy**   **Activation energy**

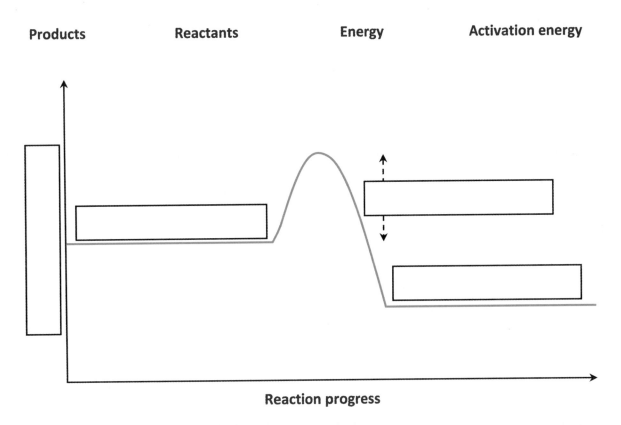

Reaction progress

(b) An exothermic reaction is one that gives *out* heat.
What is the name for the type of reaction that takes *in* heat?

5

Question 4   **(15 marks)**

The passage below is about the three states of matter.
The following five words are missing from the passage:

chemical   **conservation**   **evaporation**   **melting**   **physical**

Write the missing words in the spaces provided.

There are three states of matter: solid, liquid and gas. When a solid is heated it turns into a

liquid – this change of state is called _____. When a liquid is heated it turns

into a gas – this change of state is called _____.

Liquid water freezes to become solid ice; this is an example of a _____

change. However, when electricity is passed through liquid water it is converted into its

elements, hydrogen and oxygen; this is an example of a _____ change.

When liquid water freezes, the mass of the ice formed is the same as the mass of the liquid

water. This is an example of _____ of mass.

Question 5   (15 marks)

A student used the circuit diagram on the right to
investigate how the current flowing through
resistor **R** varies with the voltage (potential
difference) across it.

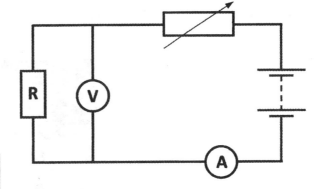

(a) **A** is an ammeter.
        Does an ammeter measure current or
        voltage?

┌───┐
│   │
└───┘

(b) The student found that the current flowing through the resistor was proportional to the
        voltage across it.
        Which graph, **X** or **Y**, shows that current is proportional to voltage?
        Justify your answer.

Graph X   **Graph Y**

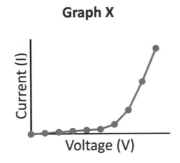   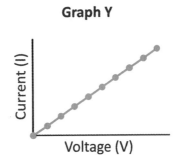

┌──┐
│   │
├──┤
│   │
├──┤
│   │
└──┘

(c) A current of 6 A flows through the resistor when a voltage of 12 V is applied across it.
        Calculate the resistance of the resistor.
        Include the unit in your answer.

┌──┐
│ Calculation   │
│   │
│   │
│   │
│   │
│   │
└──┘

Question 6   **(15 marks)**

In ecology, each of the pieces of equipment shown below can be used in a habitat study.

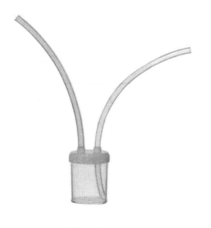  

      Pooter   **Net**   **Pitfall trap**

(a) Circle the name of one of these pieces of equipment and describe how you would use it.

(b) Name two resources that trees, such as those shown on the right, compete for.

(c) Describe one way we can help to conserve ecological biodiversity.

8

Question 7

The graph below shows how the speed of a car changed with time during a journey.

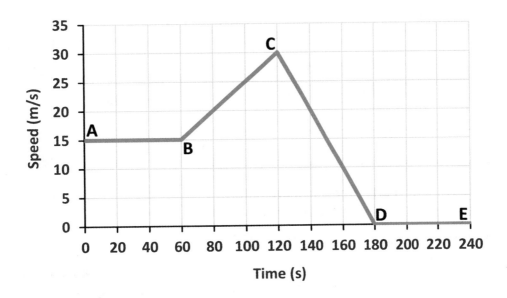

(a) What is the maximum speed of the car during this journey?

(b) Calculate the acceleration of the car between positions **B** and **C**.

Calculation

(c) Describe the motion of the car between positions **C** and **D**.

(d) Describe the motion of the car between positions **D** and **E**.

9

Question 8 **(15 marks)**

The diagram shows an experiment a student carried out to investigate the reaction between an acid and a base.

(a) Name a base that could be used in this investigation.

```
[                                    ]
```

(b) Name an acid that could be used in this investigation.

```
[                                    ]
```

(c) The diagram shows a pH probe and a pH meter, which the student used in this experiment.

Answer the following question by putting a tick (✓) in the correct box.

At the start of the experiment, the reading on the pH meter should be:

Less than 7   ☐

7   ☐

Greater than 7   ☐

(d) Another student decided to use an indicator, instead of using a pH meter, to investigate the reaction between an acid and a base.

    (i) Name an indicator that could be used in this experiment.

```
[                                                            ]
```

    (ii) What colour is this indicator when added to a base?

```
[                                                            ]
```

(a) Complete the table below, using the Periodic Table of the elements to predict the ratio of atoms and the chemical formula for each of the compounds listed.

You should refer to page 79 of the *Formulae and Tables* booklet when answering this question.

The first row is completed for you.

Compound	First element	Second element	Ratio	Formula
Magnesium chloride	Magnesium (Mg)	Chlorine (Cl)	1 : 2	$MgCl_2$
Potassium chloride	Potassium (K)	Chlorine (Cl)	:	
Hydrogen sulfide	Hydrogen (H)	Sulfur (S)	:	
Aluminium oxide	Aluminium (Al)	Oxygen (O)	:	

(b) Aluminium is a metal but sulfur is a non-metal.
Outline two differences between metals and non-metals.

Question 10 (15 marks)

In 1932, the Irish physicist Ernest Walton and the English physicist John Cockroft produced the first artificial splitting of a nucleus by bombarding atoms of lithium with high speed protons.

Walton and Cockroft showed that mass is converted into energy when a nucleus is split. This was the first experimental proof of Albert Einstein's famous equation, $E = mc^2$.

The photograph shows Walton carrying out this experiment.
For their work, Walton and Cockroft won the Nobel Prize in physics in 1951.

Courtesy of and copyright: Cavendish Laboratory, University of Cambridge.

(a) Protons are one type of particle found in the nucleus of an atom.

    (i) Name the other type of particle found in the nucleus of an atom.

    (ii) Compare the charge of the proton with the charge of the other particle you have named.

(b) In the space below, draw a labelled diagram of an atom of lithium showing the positions of the nucleus and the electrons.

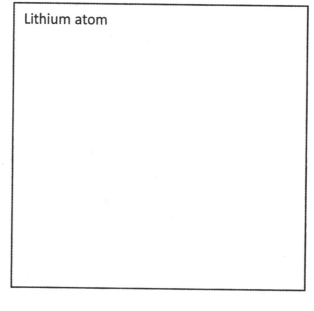

Lithium atom

The work of Walton and Cockroft saw the dawn of the nuclear age.

(c) State one advantage of using nuclear power to generate electricity.

Additional writing space for **Section A**.
Label all work clearly with the question number and part.

Question 11 **(30 marks)**

The diagram below shows how carbon moves into and out of the air and soil.
This is part of the carbon cycle.

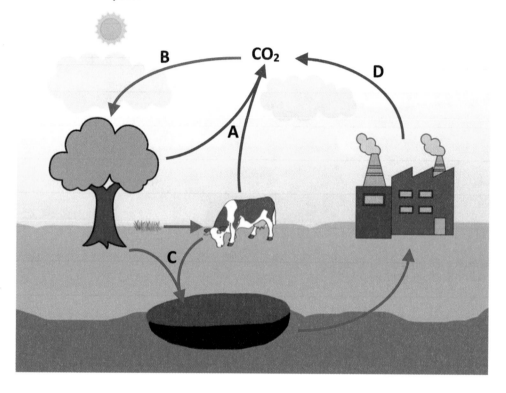

(a) During process **A**, plants and animals release carbon dioxide (CO_2) into the air.
Name process **A**.

(b) During process **B**, plants take in carbon dioxide from the air to make food.

(i) Name process **B**.

(ii) Complete the chemical equation below for process **B**.
You may use either the name or the chemical formula for each substance to complete the equation.

Carbon dioxide (CO_2) + _____ → Glucose ($C_6H_{12}O_6$) + _____

(iii) Name the green chemical found in plants which allows process **B** to happen.

(c) Describe how plants and animals add carbon into the soil in process **C**.

(d) Process **D** shows the burning of fossil fuels, which releases carbon dioxide into the air. Name one such fuel.

(e) Carbon dioxide is often referred to as a greenhouse gas.
Describe two environmental concerns associated with an increase in the level of carbon dioxide in our atmosphere.

(f) A scientist claims that there would be no life on Earth if there was no carbon dioxide in our atmosphere.
Do you think this statement is true or false?
Justify your answer.

mrpsmg
Visit www.e-xamit.ie

15

Question 12   (45 marks)

A group of students investigated how high a ball bounces after it is dropped.
They allowed a ball to fall from a number of different drop-heights and measured how high the ball bounced each time (the bounce-height).
Their results are shown in the table below.

Drop-height (m)	Bounce-height (m)
0.5	0.2
1.0	0.4
1.5	0.6
2.0	0.8
3.0	1.2
4.0	1.6
5.0	2.0

(a)   In the space below, present this information using a suitable graph or chart.
(Your graph or chart should allow the viewer to read the results of the investigation and to see any pattern.)

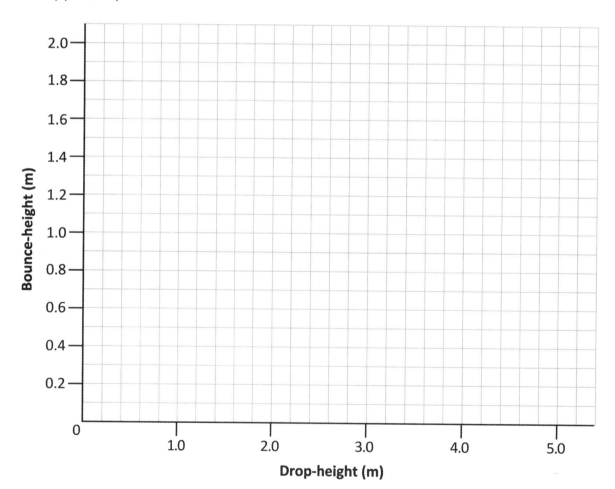

(b) If the ball was dropped from a height of 10 m, how high would you expect it to bounce?

(c) Which is easier to measure accurately, the drop-height of the ball or its bounce-height? Explain your answer.

(d) Which is easier to measure accurately, 0.2 m or 1.6 m? Explain your answer.

(e) Outline one safety precaution which the students should take when carrying out this investigation.

(f) State the main energy conversion that takes place as the ball falls through the air.

(g) A student made the following statement: "Green tennis balls bounce higher than orange tennis balls." Is this a testable hypothesis? Justify your answer.

Question 13

The article below is from a science website. Read it and answer the questions that follow.

Do Other Planets Have Solar Eclipses?

As Earthlings, we have the privilege of seeing total solar eclipses, those dazzling events in which the Moon blocks the Sun's light from hitting our planet. But is Earth the only planet in our solar system that experiences this spectacular phenomenon?

The answer is no. Total solar eclipses can happen on other planets too. To get a solar eclipse, the first thing you need is a moon. This immediately rules out total solar eclipses on Mercury or Venus – two planets without moons.

Mars has two moons, but both are too small to create a total solar eclipse that would be visible from Mars. Rather, each of these moons can make a partial eclipse – called a "ring eclipse" – for any potential life-form watching from the ground.

The *Curiosity* rover took the image shown here of a ring eclipse as Mars' largest moon, Phobos, passed directly in front of the Sun in August 2013.

The gas giants – Jupiter, Saturn, Uranus and Neptune – can all have total solar eclipses, as they have large moons and the Sun appears small to them. But because these planets are made of gas, it would be impossible to stand on them and see such solar eclipses.

Remember – never look at an eclipse without proper eye protection!

© LiveScience/Future US, Inc.

(a) **(i)** What is a solar system?

(ii) Our solar system is part of the Milky Way galaxy. What is a galaxy?

(b) **(i)** Name a planet in our solar system which has no moon.

(ii) Name Mars' largest moon.

(c) Why should you never look at an eclipse without proper eye protection?

(d) **(i)** Draw a labelled diagram to show a model of a *solar* eclipse.

(ii) Draw a labelled diagram to show a model of a *lunar* eclipse.

(e) Why does the Sun appear small when observed from the gas giant planets?

(f) Currently we use robots such as the *Curiosity* rover to explore Mars.
Outline two reasons why it is difficult for humans to explore Mars themselves.

(g) For hundreds of years, astronomers believed that the Sun orbited the Earth. We now know that to be incorrect.

Outline another example of how our scientific understanding of something has changed over time.

Question 14

(45 marks)

Bakers and food scientists are interested in the physical properties of bread.

One property they investigate is how hard or easy it is to compress (squash) the bread.

They do this by measuring the force needed to compress the bread by 1 mm, as in the photograph.

The graph below shows the force needed to compress samples of white bread and brown bread by 1 mm, and how this force changes with the age of the bread (the time since the bread was baked).

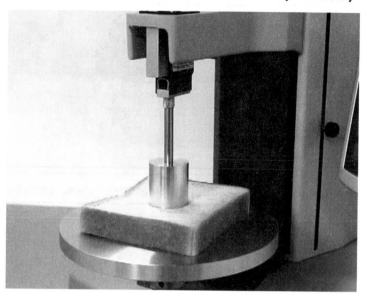

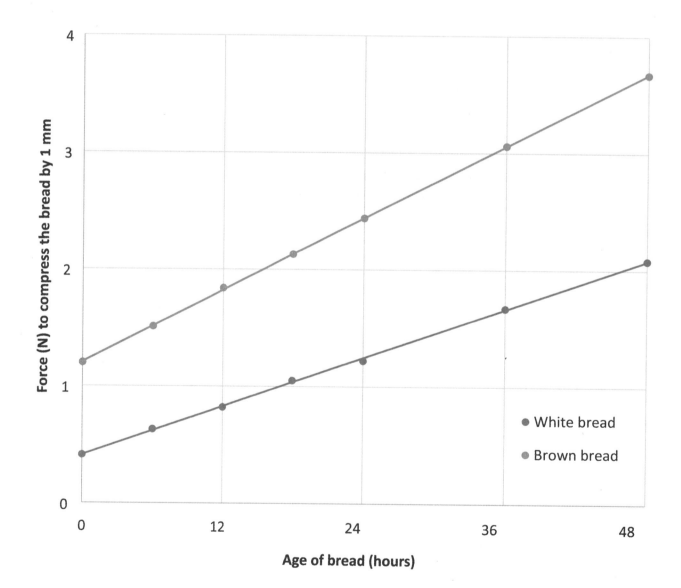

(a) What is the unit of force?

(b) Name an instrument suitable for measuring a distance of 1 mm.

(c) State two variables which must be kept constant during this experiment to ensure that it is a fair test.

(d) In the table below place a tick (✓) next to any conclusion that is supported by the graph and a cross (✗) next to any conclusion that is **not** supported by the graph.

Conclusion	✓ or ✗
White bread is easier to compress as it gets older.	
Old white bread is harder to compress than fresh brown bread.	
Brown bread is healthier for you than white bread.	
White bread becomes harder to compress faster than brown bread.	

(e) Bread is a good source of carbohydrate.
Carbohydrate is a nutrient that is an essential part of our diet.

(i) Name another essential nutrient in our diet.

(ii) Name a good source of this nutrient.

(iii) Why is this nutrient an essential part of our diet?

(f)   A boy bit off a piece of a brown bread sandwich.

A short time later, the cells in the boy's body were able to use the energy contained in the bread's carbohydrate.

Describe the processes that happened to the bread (and the carbohydrate in it) from when the boy put the bread into his mouth to when his cells used the energy in the carbohydrate.

Question 15   (45 marks)

The picture below shows a laboratory model of the human breathing system.
The bell jar represents the rib cage and the rubber sheet represents the diaphragm.

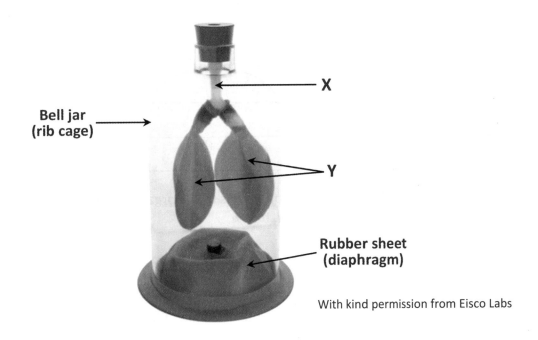

Bell jar
(rib cage)

X

Y

Rubber sheet
(diaphragm)

With kind permission from Eisco Labs

(a) **(i)** Name the part of the breathing system represented by the tube labelled **X**.

(ii) Name the part of the breathing system represented by the balloons labelled **Y**.

(b) Describe what happens to the balloons (**Y**) when the rubber sheet (diaphragm) is pulled down.

(c) Describe one flaw or limitation in this model.
Explain why this is a flaw or limitation.

(d) As the blood travels past the breathing system, some gases move between the air and the blood.

  (i) Explain why the air we breathe in contains more oxygen than the air we breathe out.

  (ii) Explain why the air we breathe in contains the same amount of nitrogen as the air we breathe out.

After it leaves the breathing system, blood travels to the organ which pumps it all around the body. This organ is shown in the diagram below.

(e) Name the organ shown.

(f) Draw arrows on the diagram to show the direction of blood flow.

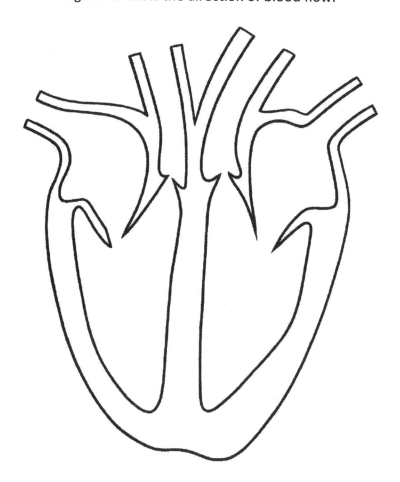

Micro-organisms such as yeast also release gases.
The photograph below shows an investigation into the factors that affect the volume of gas released by yeast.

A (5 °C)   B (20 °C)   C (35 °C)

In each case, the gas released is collected in the balloon attached to the top of the reaction flask.

Test **A** was carried out at 5 °C.

Test **B** was carried out at 20 °C.

Test **C** was carried out at 35 °C.

As the reaction temperature increased (from **A** to **C**), a greater volume of gas was collected in the balloon.

(g) Suggest two reasons why an increase in reaction temperature might lead to an increase in the volume of gas collected.

(h) Describe one positive role and one negative role which micro-organisms play in human health.

Additional writing space for **Section B**.
Label all work clearly with the question number and part.

Acknowledgements

Images

Images on page 3:	pediaa.com
Images on page 4:	State Examinations Commission
Image on page 5:	State Examinations Commission
Image on page 6:	shutterstock.com
Images on page 7:	State Examinations Commission
Images on page 8:	eiscolabs.com; nms.ac.uk; treehugger.com
Image on page 9:	State Examinations Commission
Image on page 10:	chemix.org
Images on page 11:	aliexpress.com; wikipedia.org
Image on page 12:	cambridgephysics.org
Image on page 14:	sciencefacts.net
Image on page 18:	nasa.gov
Images on page 20:	youtube.com; State Examinations Commission
Image on page 22:	clipartmax.com
Image on page 23:	philipharris.co.uk
Image on page 24:	teleskola.mt
Image on page 25:	youtube.com

Texts

Text on page 18:	Geggel, Laura. *Do Other Planets Have Solar Eclipses?* http://www.livescience.com (5 August 2017).

Material may have been adapted, for the purpose of assessment, without the authors' prior consent.

Do not write on this page

Junior Cycle Final Examination – Common Level

Science

Monday 12 June

Morning 9:30 – 11:30

Coimisiún na Scrúduithe Stáit

State Examinations Commission

Junior Cycle Final Examination 2022

Science

Common Level

Monday 13 June   Morning 9:30 – 11:30

360 marks

Examination Number

Day and Month of Birth

For example, 3rd February is entered as 0302

Centre Stamp

Instructions

Write your Examination Number and your Day and Month of Birth in the boxes on the front cover.

There are two sections in this examination paper.

| Section A | 150 marks | 10 questions |
| Section B | 210 marks | 5 questions |

Answer **all** parts of **all** questions.

You may ask the superintendent for a copy of the *Formulae and Tables* booklet. You must return it at the end of the examination. You are not allowed to bring your own copy into the examination.

Not all the questions carry equal marks. The number of marks for each question is stated at the top of the question.

Write your answers in the spaces provided in this booklet. You are not required to use all of the space provided. There is extra space at the end of Section A and at the back of the booklet. Label any extra work clearly with the question number and part.

This examination booklet will be scanned and your work will be presented to an examiner on screen. Anything that you write outside of the answer areas may not be seen by the examiner.

Write your answers in blue or black pen. You may use pencil for graphs and diagrams only.

Question 1

(15 marks)

Scientists use instruments, such as the ones shown below, to take measurements.

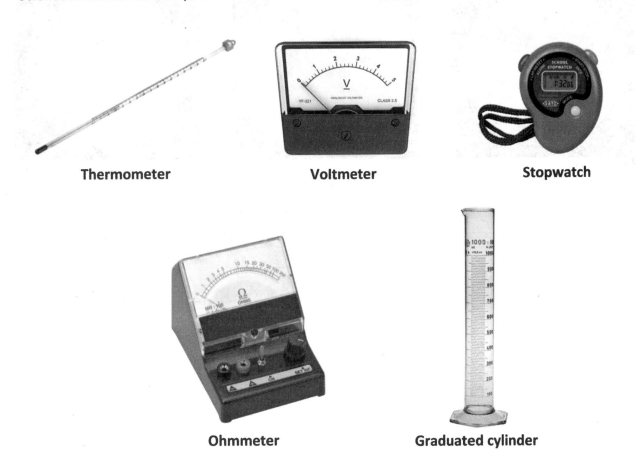

| Thermometer | Voltmeter | Stopwatch |

| Ohmmeter | Graduated cylinder |

For each of the physical quantities named in the table below, choose an instrument shown above that is used to measure that physical quantity.

Physical Quantity	Instrument
Volume	
Time	
Temperature	
Resistance	
Potential difference	

Question 2   **(15 marks)**

The images below show three celestial objects found in our solar system.
The objects are not shown on the same scale.

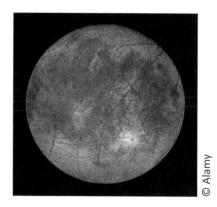

Moon

Star

Planet

(a) Match the name of each celestial object with the correct description in the table below.

Description	Name of celestial object
Consists of burning gas	
Orbits a planet	
Orbits a star	

(b) Which of the celestial objects above has the largest diameter?

(c) Draw a labelled diagram to show the positions of a moon, a star and a planet during a lunar eclipse, i.e., an eclipse of the moon.

Question 3 (15 marks)

An atom of element **X** is shown in the diagram.

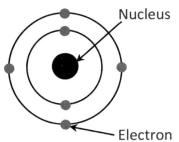

Nucleus

Electron

2022

(a) Name one subatomic particle found in the nucleus of an atom.

(b) Answer the following question by putting a tick (✓) in the correct box.

The charge on the electron is:

Positive ☐   Negative ☐   Neutral ☐

(c) Place an **X** on the Periodic Table shown below to indicate the position of element **X**.
You may use the Periodic Table on page 79 of the *Formulae and Tables* booklet to help you answer this question.

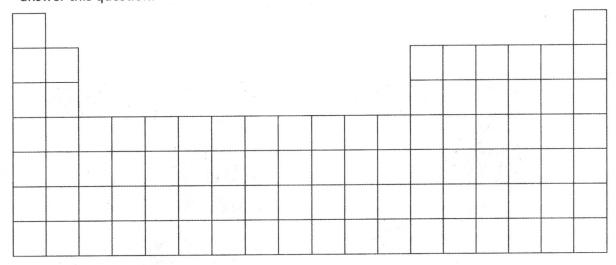

(d) Element **X** forms a compound with hydrogen. Element **X** is shown in grey. Hydrogen is shown in green. Circle the diagram below which represents the compound formed. Justify your answer.

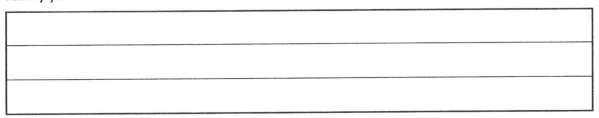

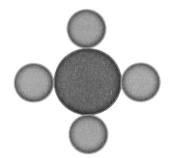

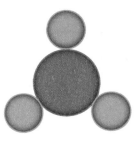

Ixytex
Visit www.e-xamit.ie

33

Question 4 (15 marks)

The theory of evolution by natural selection describes how organisms evolve and change over generations.

(a) A student made the following statements about the theory of evolution by natural selection. Indicate if each of the statements is true or false by putting a tick (✓) in the correct column.

Statement	True	False
Evolution involves genetic mutations.		
Natural selection is based on competition.		
Natural selection involves survival of the weakest.		

Organisms can evolve and adapt, making them better suited to their environment. The organisms pictured below have adaptations that help them survive in their habitats. A fox is an omnivore (an animal that eats plant and animal matter). A rose bush is an autotroph (an organism that makes its own food).

Fox

Rose bush

(b) Describe one way a fox is adapted to help it survive in its habitat.

(c) Describe one way a rose bush is adapted to help it survive in its habitat.

Question 5

Water is a colourless, tasteless substance. Water contains hydrogen and oxygen chemically combined.

(a) The picture on the right shows a model of a water molecule. The chemical formula for water is H_2O. Does the red sphere in the model represent hydrogen or oxygen?

[   ]

© Shutterstock

(b) In the diagram below both beakers contain pure water at 20 °C. Which one of the properties listed below is the same for the water in each beaker? Put a tick (✓) in the correct box.

Mass   ☐

Weight   ☐

Density   ☐

Volume   ☐

A student investigated the solubility of a compound in water. She added some of the compound to 50 cm³ of water at 20 °C and stirred the mixture until the compound was completely dissolved. She repeated this until no more of the compound dissolved. She found that the greatest mass of the compound that she was able to dissolve was 15 g.

(c) Calculate the solubility of the compound in g/cm^3.

Calculation

(d) Describe two things that the student could have done to allow a greater mass of the compound to be dissolved.

Question 6   **(15 marks)**

The photographs below show the Moon as seen from the Earth at certain times during the lunar cycle. The images are not in the correct order.

Image 1	Image 2	Image 3	Image 4

Answer questions **(a)**, **(b)** and **(c)** by putting a tick (✓) in the correct box.

(a) Which image, **1**, **2**, **3** or **4**, shows a New Moon?

Image **1** ☐   Image **2** ☐   Image **3** ☐   Image **4** ☐

(b) Which image, **1**, **2**, **3** or **4**, shows the Moon during a waxing crescent phase?

Image **1** ☐   Image **2** ☐   Image **3** ☐   Image **4** ☐

(c) Approximately how long is the lunar cycle?

1 day ☐   1 week ☐   1 month ☐   1 year ☐

(d) Explain why the Moon is visible from Earth.

(e) An object weighs less on the Moon than on Earth.
Put a tick (✓) in the box next to the sentence that explains why:

It is colder on the Moon than on Earth. ☐

The Moon has a smaller radius than Earth. ☐

The Moon has a smaller mass than Earth. ☐

The Moon has no atmosphere. ☐

Question 7   **(15 marks)**

A trolley moves along a horizontal track. The distance of the trolley from its starting point was measured every second for 8 seconds. The results are shown in the graph below.

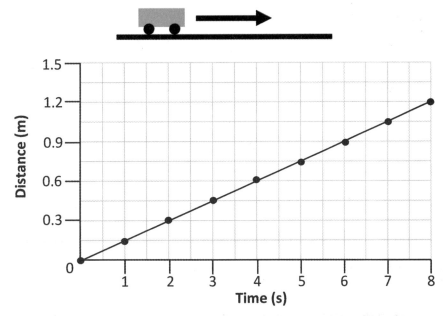

(a)   Calculate the average speed of the trolley. Include the unit for your answer.

Calculation

The student carried out a second distance-time investigation when the track was sloped.

(b)   Write a suitable hypothesis for this second investigation.

(c)   The student wanted to be able to make a fair comparison between the two investigations. Describe one thing the student should have done to allow a fair comparison.

(d)   On the graph above, sketch the expected result for **your** hypothesis.

Question 8 (15 marks)

During your studies you learned about a scientific model that helps us understand the origin of the universe.

(a) Name the model you studied.

Outline two pieces of evidence that support this model.

In September 2021, the SpaceX Inspiration4 mission successfully orbited the Earth. This was the world's first all-civilian space mission and represents a new era for human space exploration.

(b) Outline one benefit and one hazard of space exploration.

Benefit:

Hazard:

Question 9 (15 marks)

A student was given two acids, **S** and **T**. He set up the apparatus shown below to investigate how the pH of **S** and **T** changed when they reacted with a base. The diagrams below show the pH of **S** and **T** at the start of the investigation.

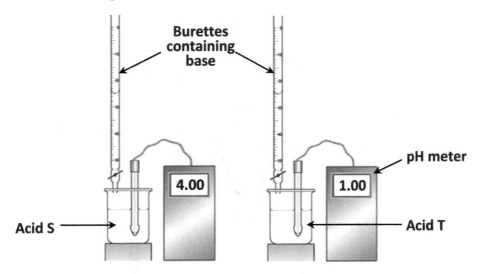

pH readings at the start of the investigation

(a) Which acid, **S** or **T**, was more acidic at the start of the investigation?

(b) State one safety precaution the student should have followed when handling the acids.

The student opened the tap on each burette and allowed the base to flow into the beakers of acid. The changes in pH were recorded as the base was added. The graph shows both sets of results.

(c) What was the pH of the solutions when 50 cm³ of base had been added?

(d) What is the pH of a neutral solution?

(e) Identify a laboratory base the student could have used in this investigation.

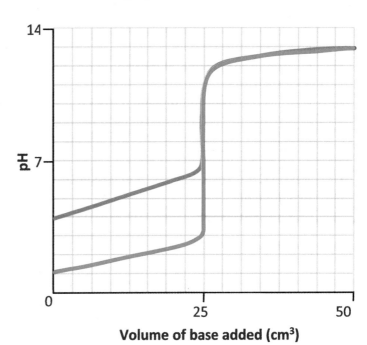

Question 10 (15 marks)

The diagram shows the human heart and some of the blood vessels of the circulatory system.
The arrows indicate the direction in which the blood flows as it travels around the body.

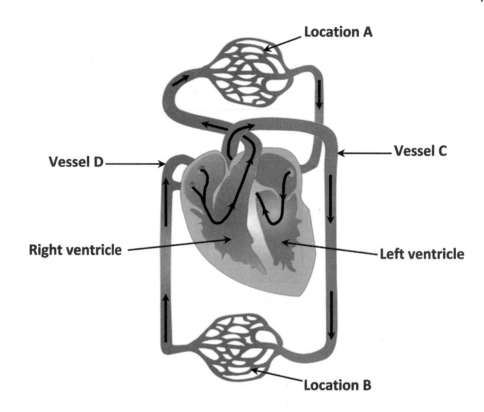

Location A

Vessel D

Vessel C

Right ventricle

Left ventricle

Location B

(a) The table below lists statements about the diagram.
Indicate if each statement is true or false by putting a tick (✓) in the correct column.

Statement	True	False
The blood in vessel **C** is deoxygenated.		
The organs found at location **A** are part of the respiratory system.		
Carbon dioxide leaves the blood at location **B**.		
Vessel **D** is a vein.		

(b) Vessel **C** has thicker walls than vessel **D**.
Explain why.

2022

Question 11   **(30 marks)**

The diagram shows the movement of the Earth around the Sun. The letters **A**, **B**, **C** and **D** represent four positions of the Earth as it moves around the Sun.

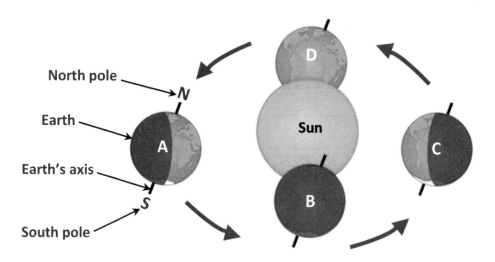

(a) Starting at position **A**, what will be the position of the Earth when 18 months have passed? Put a tick (✓) in the correct box.

Position **A** ☐   Position **B** ☐   Position **C** ☐   Position **D** ☐

(b) Which letter, **A**, **B**, **C** or **D**, represents the position of the Earth during summer in the northern hemisphere? Justify your answer.

(c) Select a letter, **A**, **B**, **C** or **D**, which represents a position of the Earth when day and night last approximately the same length of time.

Position **A** ☐   Position **B** ☐   Position **C** ☐   Position **D** ☐

(d) Which one of the following statements explains why seasons occur on Earth? Put a tick (✓) in the correct box.

The Moon moves around its axis.   ☐

The tilted Earth moves around the Sun.   ☐

The tilted Earth moves around its axis.   ☐

There are sunspots on the surface of the Sun.   ☐

The length of the shadow cast by an object depends on the position of the Sun in the sky. Two groups of students in Ireland, group **A** and group **B**, investigated how the length of a shadow varied over a year. The graph below shows the results obtained by group **A**, who used a pole to cast the shadow.

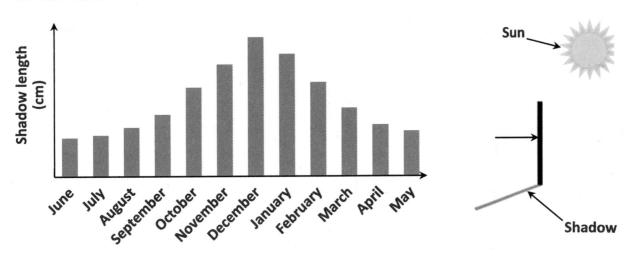

(e) Name an instrument the students could have used to measure the length of the shadow.

(f) State one variable the students in group **A** should have kept constant.

(g) Group **B** carried out the same investigation, but instead of using a pole to create a shadow, they used a student from the group.
Which group, **A** or **B**, carried out a better investigation? Justify your answer.

(h) Group **A** also investigated how the length of the shadow cast by the pole changed during a sunny day in June.

Using the axes on the right, sketch the curve the students should have obtained.

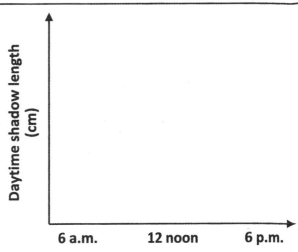

43

Question 12   **(30 marks)**

The diagram illustrates the organisation of genetic information within human cells.
Some of the labels are missing.

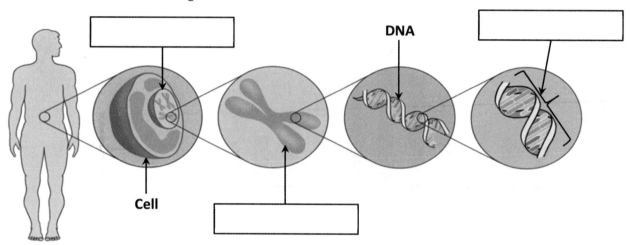

DNA

Cell

(a) Use each of the words listed below to complete the labels on the diagram above.

       Chromosome   **Nucleus**   **Gene**

(b) Name an instrument which could be used in the laboratory to view human cells.

A normal human brain cell contains 46 chromosomes.
Answer questions **(c)** and **(d)** by putting a tick (✓) in the correct box.

(c) How many chromosomes are present in a human sperm cell?

       23 ☐

       46 ☐

       69 ☐

       92 ☐

(d) The sperm cell fertilises an egg cell. How many chromosomes should be present in the
resulting zygote?

       23 ☐

       46 ☐

       69 ☐

       92 ☐

(e) Coat colour in a breed of dog is controlled by a single gene. There are two possible versions (alleles) of this gene – black coat (**B**) and white coat (**b**). The gene for black coat is dominant to the gene for white coat.

In their cells, dogs contain two versions of the gene for coat colour. Possible pairs are **BB** (black), **Bb** (black) and **bb** (white).

The table below illustrates a genetic cross between a male dog with genotype **Bb** and a female dog with genotype **bb**. The table is incomplete.

	Male dog	Female dog
Parent genotype	Bb	bb
Sex cells produced	B or b	b
Offspring genotype	◯ or ◯	

(i) Complete the table by writing the two possible genotypes of the offspring that could result from this cross.

(ii) What is the probability of the offspring having a black coat?
Put a tick (✓) in the correct box.

0% ☐   25% ☐   50% ☐   75% ☐   100% ☐

(iii) If a different male dog, with genotype **BB**, was bred with the same female dog, what would be the probability of their offspring having a black coat?
Put a tick (✓) in the correct box.

0% ☐   25% ☐   50% ☐   75% ☐   100% ☐

Question 13

(45 marks)

A student carried out a series of experiments to investigate the properties of sucrose (table sugar).

In the first experiment, the student investigated the melting point of sucrose.

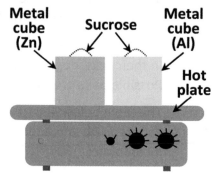

Two metal cubes of equal volume were placed on a hotplate as shown in the diagram. One was made of zinc (**Zn**) and the other was made of aluminium (**Al**). One gram of sucrose was placed on top of each cube and the hotplate was turned on.

(a) What is meant by the melting point of a substance?

(b) Is melting an example of a physical change or a chemical change? Explain your answer.

(c) The aluminium cube had a smaller mass than the zinc cube. Explain why.

(d) The sucrose on the aluminium melted before the sucrose on the zinc. What does this result tell us about the two metals? Put a tick (✓) in the correct box.

Aluminium is a better conductor of heat than zinc. ☐

Aluminium has a higher melting point than zinc. ☐

Aluminium is less reactive than zinc. ☐

Aluminium atoms have less neutrons than zinc atoms. ☐

(e) Explain why the sugar melted but the metals did not.

(f) The dials on the hotplate were made of plastic, a non-metal. State two properties of non-metals.

In the second experiment the student dissolved sucrose in water. They used some of the following components to investigate if the resulting solution could conduct electricity.

Buzzer   **Wires**   **Bulb**   **Battery**

(g) Using electrical circuit symbols, draw a labelled diagram of a circuit the student could have used to carry out this investigation. You may use the symbols on pages 72 – 78 of the *Formulae and Tables* booklet to help you answer this question.

Labelled diagram

(h) The student was then given the task of separating the sucrose from the water.
Describe how the student could have separated these two substances.
You should include a labelled diagram in your answer **and** indicate the location of the sucrose at the end of the separation.

Labelled diagram

deljoc
Visit www.e-xamit.ie

47

Question 14 (45 marks)

Read the following article, adapted from a European Union (EU) website, and answer the questions that follow.

The European Green Deal outlines a plan to make Europe the first climate-neutral continent by 2050. This involves boosting the economy, caring for nature, and improving our health and quality of life. The *Farm to Fork Strategy* is at the heart of the Green Deal. It addresses the challenges of sustainable food systems and recognises the links between healthy people, healthy societies and a healthy planet.

We need to do much more to keep ourselves and the planet healthy. The increasing occurrence of droughts, floods, forest fires, and new pests are a constant reminder that our food system is under threat and must become more sustainable.

Since 1990, EU agriculture has reduced its greenhouse gas emissions by 20%. However, food systems remain one of the key drivers of climate change and environmental degradation. The European Commission aims to further reduce greenhouse gas emissions from agriculture by 2050.

The move towards a sustainable food system will not happen without a shift in our diets. It is essential to take action to change consumption patterns and reduce food waste. While about 20% of the food we produce is wasted, obesity is also rising. Over half of the adult population are now overweight, contributing to a high occurrence of diet-related diseases and related healthcare costs.

Farm to Fork Strategy, European Union, May 2020

(a) State one aim of the European Green Deal.

(b) Name a natural phenomenon which threatens our food supply system.

(c) **(i)** EU agriculture has reduced its greenhouse gas emissions by 20% since 1990. Name a greenhouse gas which drives climate change and is produced by agricultural practices.

(ii) Describe an initiative that could be undertaken to reduce the production of this gas.

48

(d) 20% of the food we produce is not eaten.
Suggest one way in which a household could reduce its food waste.

Human health is affected by environmental factors such as nutrition.
The table below compares the nutritional value of two similar foods, **Food A** and **Food B**.

Nutrient	Food A Mass per 80 g serving	Food B Mass per 80 g serving
Sugar	18 g	7 g
Saturated fat	7 g	3 g
Cholesterol	55 mg	33 mg
Sodium	330 mg	200 mg
Protein	12 g	20 g

(e) Identify one piece of evidence from the table which shows that the two foods were compared fairly.

(f) Which food, **A** or **B**, would be a better choice as part of a healthy diet? Use two pieces of evidence from the table to support your answer.

(g) Calculate the percentage protein in food **A**.

Calculation

(h) Food is broken down in the digestive system. The diagram below shows the anatomy of the human digestive system and some of its associated organs.

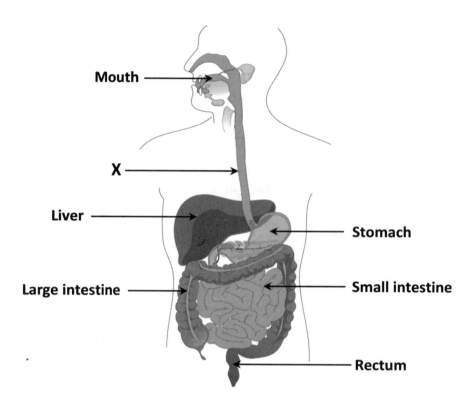

(i) On the diagram, draw a circle around a part of the digestive system which is also a part of the respiratory system.

(ii) Identify structure **X**.

(iii) Complete the table below by matching the part of the digestive system from the diagram with its function.

Function	Part of digestive system
Absorbs water from fully-digested matter	
Secretes hydrochloric acid to kill bacteria in food	
Absorbs fully-digested food into the bloodstream	

Question 15   **(60 marks)**

Energy exists in many forms. The energy stored by an object due to its position or shape is called potential energy. The energy of an object due to its motion is called kinetic energy.

Potential energy is converted to kinetic energy when a person jumps on a trampoline.
The diagrams show the position of a person at certain times while jumping.

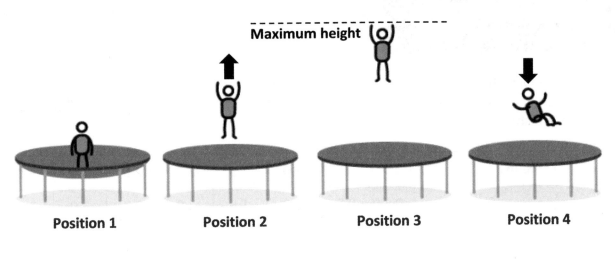

Position 1   Position 2   Position 3   Position 4

(a)   Answer the following questions by putting a tick (✓) in the correct box.

   (i)   Identify a position where the person has least kinetic energy.

       Position **1** ☐   Position **2** ☐   Position **3** ☐   Position **4** ☐

   (ii)   Identify a position where the trampoline has its greatest potential energy.

       Position **1** ☐   Position **2** ☐   Position **3** ☐   Position **4** ☐

(b)   Name a force responsible for the motion of the person in position **4**.

(c)   Heat energy is also produced when a person uses a trampoline.
       Describe one possible source of this heat energy.

An experiment was carried out to investigate the relationship between the length of a trampoline spring and the force applied to it.

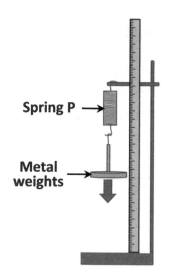

The experiment was carried out using spring **P** as shown. It was then repeated using spring **Q**, taken from a different trampoline.

Forces were applied to the springs by attaching known weights. The extension of the springs was calculated for each force applied. The results are shown in the table.

Force (N)		0	0.5	1.0	1.5	2.0	2.5	3.0	3.5
Extension (cm)	**Spring P**	0	0.5	1.0	1.5	2.0	2.5	3.0	3.5
	Spring Q	0	1.0	2.0	3.0	4.0	5.0	6.0	7.0

(d) In the space below, draw a line graph of force against extension for **each** spring.

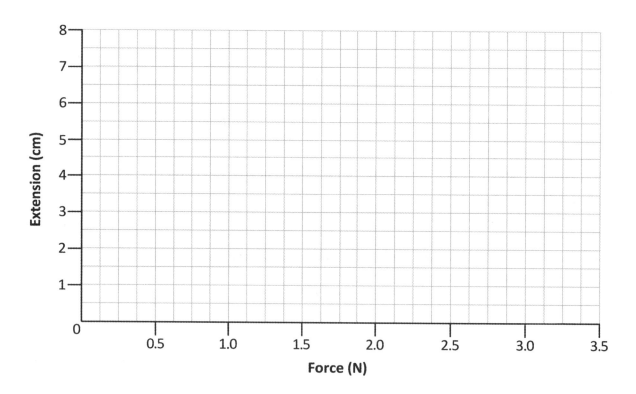

(e) State two conclusions supported by the graphs you have drawn.

(f) Spring **Q** had a length of 11 cm before any force was applied to it.
Calculate its total length when a force of 1.25 N was applied.

Calculation

(g) On Earth, a <u>mass</u> of 128 g has a <u>weight</u> of approximately 1.25 N.
Explain the underlined terms.

(h) A trampoline manufacturer is trying to decide which spring, **P** or **Q**, to use when making a new trampoline.
Which spring, **P** or **Q**, stores more energy when it is stretched by 3 cm?
Justify your answer.

2022

Acknowledgements

Images

Images on page 31:	ie.rs-online.com; indiamart.com; ldalearning.com; pharmasystems.com
Images on page 32:	wikipedia.org
Images on page 33:	State Examinations Commission
Images on page 34:	flickr.com; edutopia.org
Images on page 35:	shutterstock.com; twinkl.ie
Images on page 36:	nasa.gov
Images on page 37:	State Examinations Commission
Image on page 38:	nasaspaceflight.com
Image on page 39:	wiley.com
Image on page 40:	springer.com
Image on page 42:	shutterstock.com
Image on page 43:	State Examinations Commission
Image on page 44:	anatomyofevolution.com
Image on page 45:	lockwoodresource.com
Image on page 46:	State Examinations Commission
Image on page 50:	thinglink.com
Image on page 51:	tcschools.org
Images on page 52:	protrampolines.com; keystagewiki.com

Text

Text on page 48:	*Farm to Fork Strategy,* European Union, May 2020.

Material may have been adapted, for the purpose of assessment, without the authors' prior consent.

Do not write on this page

Junior Cycle Final Examination – Common Level

Science

Monday 13 June

Morning 9:30 – 11:30

2022J057C1EL2828

Coimisiún na Scrúduithe Stáit
State Examinations Commission

Junior Cycle Final Examination 2019

Science

Common Level

Monday 10 June   Afternoon 2:00 – 4:00

360 marks

Examination number				

Centre stamp

Instructions

Write your examination number in the box on the front cover.

There are two sections in this examination paper.

Section A	150 marks	10 questions
Section B	210 marks	6 questions

Answer **all** parts of **all** questions.

You may ask the superintendent for a copy of the *Formulae and Tables* booklet. You must return it at the end of the examination. You are not allowed to bring your own copy into the examination.

Not all the questions carry equal marks. The number of marks for each question is stated at the top of the question.

Write your answers in the spaces provided in this booklet. You are not required to use all of the space provided. There is extra space at the end of Section A and at the back of the booklet. Label any extra work clearly with the question number and part.

This examination booklet will be scanned and your work will be presented to an examiner on screen. Anything that you write outside of the answer areas may not be seen by the examiner.

Write your answers in blue or black pen. You may use pencil for graphs and diagrams only.

Question 1

(15 marks)

The diagram shows an animal cell.

(a) Use the words listed below to label the parts of the cell.

Cytoplasm   **Cell membrane**   **Nucleus**

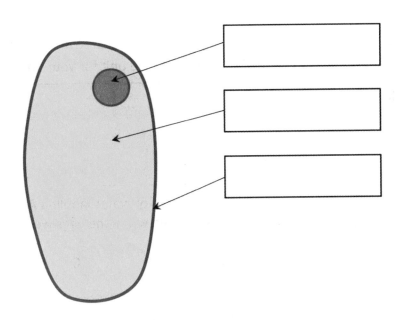

(b) Which of the three named parts controls the activities of the cell?

(c) A student was asked to examine animal cells in the laboratory. Which of the following instruments should the student use? Place a tick (✓) in the correct box.

Telescope ☐

Microscope ☐

Periscope ☐

Question 2

A student was asked to measure the density of a block.

The dimensions of the block are shown in the diagram.

The mass of the block is 128 g.

(15 marks)

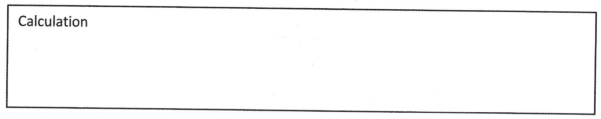

4 cm   128 g

8 cm   2 cm

(a) Calculate the volume of the block.

Calculation

(b) Calculate the density of the block. Include the unit for your answer.

Calculation

(c) The photograph below shows three glasses of water labelled **A**, **B** and **C**. An egg was placed into each glass. The photograph was taken when the eggs were stationary.

A   B   C

Which glass (**A**, **B** or **C**) contains the egg with the greatest density?

Give a reason for your answer.

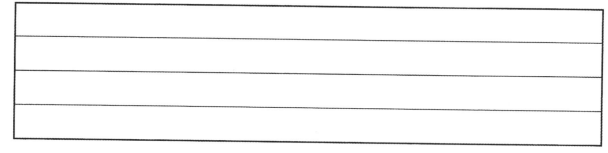

60

Question 3

The diagram below illustrates the water cycle.

Some of the key stages of the water cycle are labelled **1**, **2**, **3** and **4**.

2019

(a) Complete the table below using the numbers **1**, **2**, **3** or **4** to match each of the labelled processes shown in the diagram with the correct description.

Process	1, 2, 3 or 4?
Air currents cause clouds to move onshore	
Water falls to the Earth as precipitation	
Heat from the Sun converts liquid water into water vapour	
Plants lose water through the process of transpiration	

(b) In 2018 Ireland experienced low rainfall throughout the year. This led to water shortages and restrictions on water use.

Describe one way in which water usage in a home could be reduced.

Question 4

Natural gas contains methane (CH_4). Methane is a fuel.

Methane burns in oxygen to produce carbon dioxide and water.

The diagram below represents the reaction.

ceehsx
Visit www.e-xamit.ie

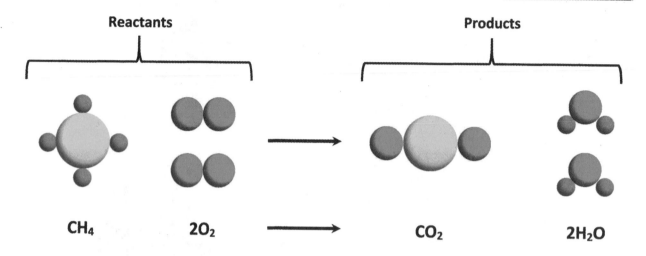

Reactants   **Products**

CH_4 $2O_2$ ⟶ CO_2 $2H_2O$

(a) Count the number of each type of atom in the products to complete the table below.

Element	Type of atom	Number of atoms in reactants	Number of atoms in products
Carbon		1	
Hydrogen		4	
Oxygen		4	

(b) Mass is conserved during this reaction. What evidence is there for this?

(c) The burning of methane is an example of a chemical change.
Describe one difference between a physical change and a chemical change.

Question 5 (15 marks)

Sickle cell anaemia is an inherited human disease. It causes the body to produce red blood cells that have an irregular shape. The gene for the disease is passed on from generation to generation.

Examine the pattern of inheritance for sickle cell anaemia shown in the family tree below and answer the questions that follow.

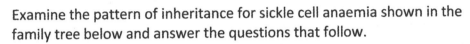

□ Male **not** suffering with sickle cell anaemia	
■ Male suffering with sickle cell anaemia	
○ Female **not** suffering with sickle cell anaemia	
● Female suffering with sickle cell anaemia	

(a) Square **1** and circle **2** are a married couple. How many children did this couple have?

(b) Some non-sufferers may be carriers of the disease. This means that they have inherited the sickle cell gene, but they don't suffer from the disease. What evidence is there from the diagram that persons **6** and **7** are both carriers?

(c) Suffering from sickle cell anaemia is an example of a genetically controlled characteristic. Classify the characteristics below as being either genetically controlled or **not** genetically controlled by placing a tick (✓) in the correct column in each case.

Characteristic	Genetically controlled	Not genetically controlled
Eye colour		
How to cycle a bike		

(d) Answer the following question by placing a tick (✓) in the correct box.

The function of red blood cells is to

Fight infection ☐   Clot blood ☐   Carry oxygen ☐

Question 6

(15 marks)

A student carried out an experiment to investigate the reaction between an acid and a base.

A pH indicator and a thermometer were used to monitor changes in pH and temperature during the reaction.

(a) Name a pH indicator the student could have used during this investigation.

(b) What colour is this indicator when placed in acid?

(c) When an acid and a base react, they neutralise each other to produce a neutral solution. On the pH scale, what number represents a neutral solution?

(d) The student noted a rise in temperature as the acid-base reaction took place. Is this an example of an endothermic or an exothermic reaction?

(e) The diagram shows an energy profile diagram for the reaction between an acid and a base.

On the diagram, show the activation energy for this reaction.

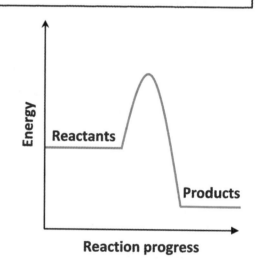

Question 7

The graph below represents the journey of a cyclist.

(15 marks)

2019

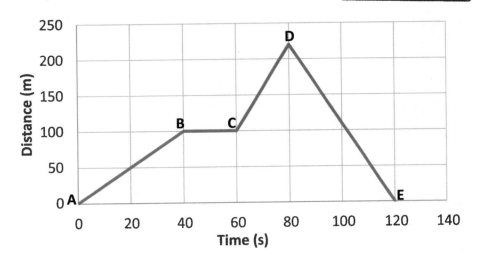

(a) Name an instrument that could be used to measure the time taken for the journey.

(b) Calculate the average speed of the cyclist as he travelled from point **A** to point **B**.

Calculation

(c) Describe the cyclist's motion between points **B** and **C** of his journey.

(d) The cyclist's speed as he travelled from point **A** to point **B** was less than his speed as he travelled from point **C** to point **D**. What evidence is there in the graph to support this?

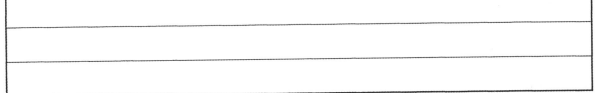

(e) Describe what the cyclist did at point **D**.

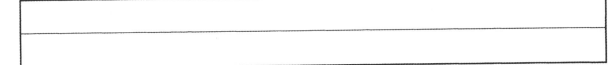

65

Question 8

(15 marks)

Global warming can cause the melting of ice sheets and glaciers, which is partly responsible for rising sea levels.

(a)   Name a human activity which has led to global warming.

(b)   State a consequence of rising sea levels on coastal areas.

(c)   Ice sheets are the natural habitat of animals such as polar bears. State one adaptation of polar bears that makes them suited to this habitat.

(d)   Would you expect the population of polar bears to increase or decrease as ice sheets melt?

(e)   When solid ice changes state to become liquid water, this is called melting. What name is given to the change of state when liquid water becomes solid ice?

Question 9

The diagram shows the human respiratory system.

cngvbw
Visit www.e-xamit.ie

2019

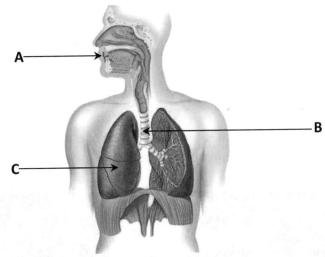

(a) Complete the table below by matching the words to the letters in the diagram.

Lung   Trachea   Liver   Oesophagus   Mouth

Letter	Part of respiratory system
A	
B	
C	

(b) Describe what happens in the respiratory system when a person breathes in.

Answer questions **(a)** and **(b)** by placing a tick (✓) in the correct box.

(a)   A star and all of the objects that orbit it is called a

Moon ☐   Solar system ☐   Galaxy ☐

(b)   A system of billions of stars is called a

Moon ☐   Solar system ☐   Galaxy ☐

(c)   The image below shows a planet passing in front of a star. This partial eclipse is called a transit. The brightness of the light detected from the star decreases as the planet transits the star and blocks its light.

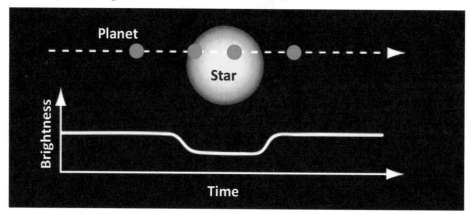

The graphs below show how the brightness of a star changed over time as two planets, **A** and **B**, transited the same star.

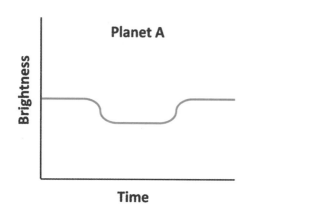
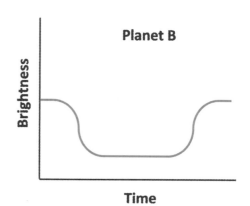

Which planet, **A** or **B**, took the shortest time to transit the star?

Which planet, **A** or **B**, is the largest? Give a reason for your answer.

2019

Question 11   **(30 marks)**

Sodium chloride (table salt) is a white crystalline solid.

Water is a solvent with a boiling point of 100 °C.

Sodium chloride can dissolve in water.

A student was asked to investigate what effect adding salt has on the boiling point of water.

(a)   Write a suitable hypothesis for this investigation.

(b)   What is meant by the boiling point of a substance?

(c)   The laboratory instrument used to measure the mass of the salt is shown in the photograph.

Identify this instrument.

(d)   In the space below, draw a labelled diagram of the arrangement of the apparatus used to determine the boiling point of water.

Labelled diagram

The student collected the following data for the boiling point of the solutions made when various masses of salt were dissolved in 60 cm^3 of water.

Mass of salt (g)	Boiling point (°C)					Average boiling point (°C)
0	100	101	100	100	102	100.6
2	101	104	101	100	103	101.8
4	103	105	104	106	107	
6	106	108	107	107	108	107.2
8	108	110	109	111	110	109.6

(e) Calculate the average boiling point when 4 g of salt was dissolved in 60 cm^3 of water.

> Calculation

(f) Suggest a reason why the student repeated the investigation five times for each mass of salt used.

(g) Does the data support the hypothesis you wrote in part **(a)**? Explain your answer.

Question 12 (30 marks)

When green light is shone into a red solution, such as blood, some of the light is absorbed, some is reflected and some passes straight through.

A student set up the apparatus shown below to investigate the relationship between the concentration of a red solution and how much green light passes through it.

On one side of the test tube of red solution, green light was emitted from a light emitting diode (LED).

On the other side of the test tube, a light dependent resistor (LDR) was used to detect how much green light passed through the solution.

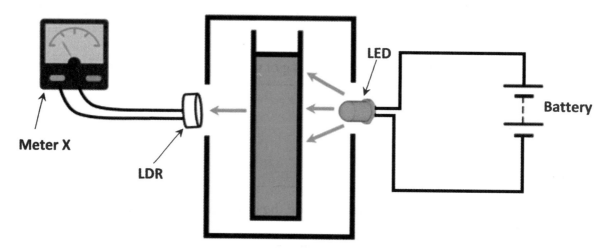

The student made different concentrations of a solution of red food dye by varying the number of drops of dye added to 20 cm³ of water. The resistance of the LDR was then determined using meter **X**. The following results were obtained.

Number of drops of food colouring	0	1	2	3	4	5	6	7	8
Resistance (Ω)	1.0	1.5	2.0	2.5	3.0	3.5	4.0	4.5	5.0

(a) In the space below, draw a graph of the results obtained.

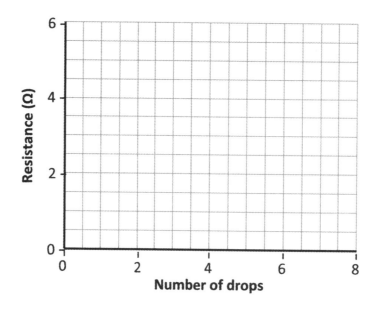

(b) State one conclusion which is supported by the results.

(c) Name meter **X**, which was used to determine the resistance of the LDR.

(d) Name a piece of equipment the student could have used to accurately measure 20 cm³ of water.

(e) A smart watch uses a green LED to measure a person's pulse by shining green light into the red blood in the person's wrist.

Describe one other technological application of physics that is used in everyday life.

(f) The chamber of the heart marked **X** pumps blood around the body and generates a pulse.

Name chamber **X**.

Explain why some of the tubes connected to the heart are coloured red and some of them are coloured blue.

Question 13

(30 marks)

Electrical energy is one of the most important types of energy that we use in our daily lives.
An electrical appliance has a power rating which tells you how much electricity it uses.

The table below shows the power rating of some common household appliances and the forms of
energy that are produced in the appliances.

Appliance	Power rating (W)	Forms of energy produced	Current used (A)
Coffee maker	1380	Heat, Sound	6
Television	115	Heat, Light, Sound	0.5
Kitchen blender	345	Heat, Kinetic, Sound	1.5
Dishwasher	2300	Heat, Kinetic, Sound	10

(a) Which appliance listed in the table uses the most electrical energy?

(b) Select one of the appliances from the table above and name a useful form of energy
produced when the appliance is being used.

Name of appliance:

Useful form of energy:

For the appliance you have selected, name an unwanted form of energy produced.

For the appliance you have selected, calculate the voltage applied across the appliance.
Include the unit for your answer.

Calculation

(c) What pattern, if any, exists between the power rating of the appliance and the current used?

Sustainability issues arise from the generation and consumption of electricity.

(d) What do you understand by the term sustainability?

(e) Suggest one way in which we can reduce how much electrical energy we use.

2019

(f) Electrical energy can be produced using renewable and non-renewable sources.
Identify **two** renewable sources of energy from the list below by placing a tick (✓) in each of the correct boxes.

Oil ☐

Solar ☐

Natural gas ☐

Wind ☐

Question 14

(30 marks)

Read the article below, adapted from an Irish newspaper, and answer the questions that follow.

UCC Study: High fibre foods ease stress effects

Interest has been growing in recent years in the link between gut bacteria and stress-related disorders. Researchers at University College Cork (UCC) have shown that micro-organisms in the gut (intestines) are really important for our brain health.

Bacteria in the gut produce fatty acids which are a source of nutrition for cells in this part of the body. Foods such as grains and vegetables contain high levels of fibre and will stimulate gut bacteria to produce these fatty acids.

The UCC study involved feeding mice the fatty acids normally produced by gut bacteria and then subjecting them to stress. Using behavioural tests, the mice were assessed for anxiety and depressive-like behaviour. The researchers found that there was a decreased level of this type of behaviour when fatty acids were consumed. These results provide new insights into mechanisms related to the impact of the gut bacteria on our brains and behaviour.

The Irish Examiner

(a) Name a type of food that is high in fibre.

(b) The study involved feeding mice fatty acids and then subjecting them to stress. Describe a control experiment which the scientists could have used in this investigation.

(c) What observation did the scientists note about the behaviour of the mice after they had been fed fatty acids?

(d) Do you agree or disagree with the use of animals (such as mice) in scientific research? Explain your answer.

76

(e) Human health is affected by environmental factors such as stress. Name another environmental factor which has an effect on human health.

(f) This article highlights a beneficial role of micro-organisms in human health. State another example of how bacteria could have an effect on human health.

(g) The image shows bacterial cells dividing in order to reproduce. This is an example of asexual reproduction.

Describe one difference between sexual and asexual reproduction.

(h) Over time a bacterial population can evolve. Outline the theory of evolution by natural selection.

Question 15

(45 marks)

The Periodic Table was developed by Dmitri Mendeleev. It was published 150 years ago in 1869. To celebrate the International Year of the Periodic Table, The European Chemical Society has designed a new kind of Periodic Table called the '90 Elements that make up everything'.

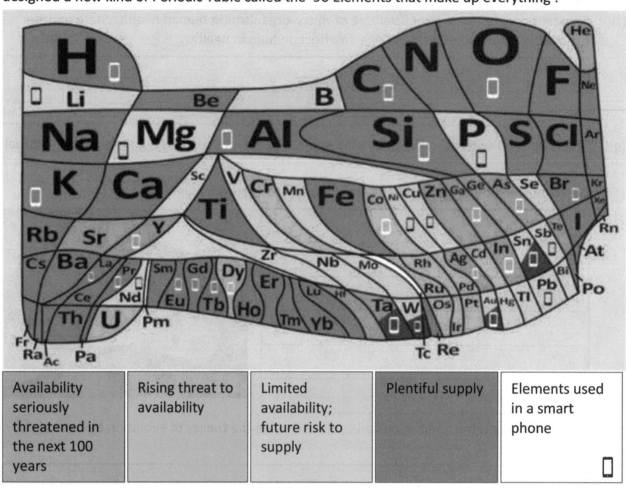

Availability seriously threatened in the next 100 years	Rising threat to availability	Limited availability; future risk to supply	Plentiful supply	Elements used in a smart phone

The table has been drawn so that the area occupied by each element indicates how much of that element is in the Earth's crust and atmosphere.

(a) From the table, identify a gas which is a component of the Earth's atmosphere and which is in plentiful supply.

(b) Why should the use of the gas helium (He) in birthday balloons be avoided?

(c) The element indium (In) is used in smart phones. At current usage rates, indium will be used up in 50 years. Suggest one way humans could contribute to sustaining levels of this element for future generations.

78

The diagrams on the right show the arrangement of particles in the elements aluminium and chlorine at room temperature.

Aluminium **Chlorine**

(d) What evidence is there in the diagrams to support the classification of these substances as elements?

(e) Which of these elements is a solid at room temperature? Justify your answer.

(f) Aluminium reacts with chlorine to form the compound aluminium chloride. Use the Periodic Table on page 79 of the *Formulae and Tables* booklet to predict the ratio of aluminium to chlorine in this compound. Hence write the chemical formula for aluminium chloride.

(g) Elements can be classified as metals or non-metals.

The table shows some of the properties of three elements from the Periodic Table.

	Melting point (°C)	Boiling point (°C)	Conductor of electricity
Element 1	1538	2862	Yes
Element 2	-7	59	No
Element 3	-101	-34	No

Which element (**1**, **2**, or **3**) is most likely to be a metal? Justify your answer.

Which element (**1**, **2**, or **3**) is a liquid at room temperature (20 °C)? Justify your answer.

Question 16

(45 marks)

2019 marks the 50th anniversary of man's first landing on the Moon. Since then there have been a number of other missions to the Moon.

(a) The diagram below shows the Earth orbiting the Sun. Complete the diagram to show the shape, location and motion of the Moon in the Earth-Sun-Moon system.

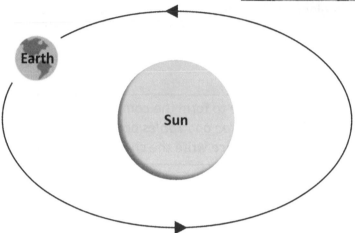

(b) At the time of the first landing, the Moon was in a waxing crescent phase as seen from Earth. The images below show different phases of the Moon in sequence, from left to right. Place a tick (✓) in the box beneath the image which shows the Moon in a waxing crescent phase.

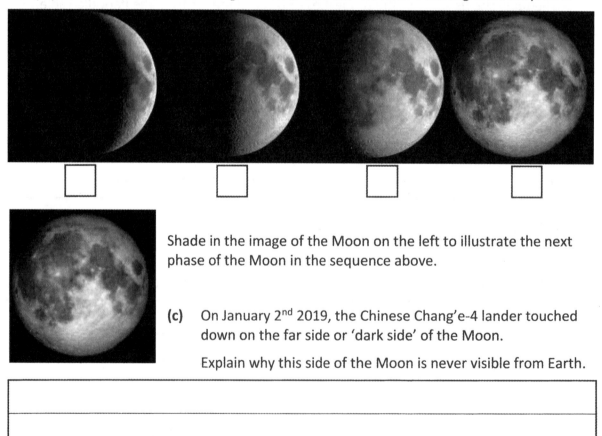

Shade in the image of the Moon on the left to illustrate the next phase of the Moon in the sequence above.

(c) On January 2nd 2019, the Chinese Chang'e-4 lander touched down on the far side or 'dark side' of the Moon.

Explain why this side of the Moon is never visible from Earth.

(d) The dark circles visible on the Moon's surface are craters. Craters occur when objects with high speed strike the surface of the Moon. Examples of such objects are asteroids and comets.

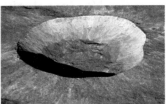

What is an asteroid?

(e) Many investigations were carried out during missions to the Moon. One investigation measured the temperature of the lunar surface at various depths. The graph shows the temperatures measured at different depths over a period of time.

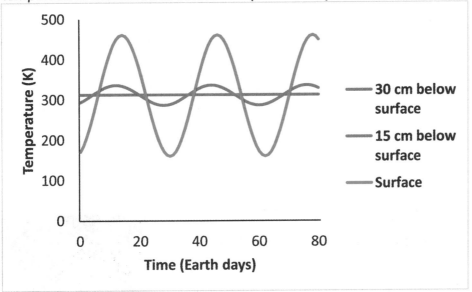

Describe how the temperature on the surface of the Moon (red line) changed with time. Suggest an explanation for this pattern.

Describe the relationship between the depth below the surface of the Moon and the change in temperature. Suggest an explanation for this relationship.

81

(f) The diagrams show the mass and weight of four objects (**A**, **B**, **C** and **D**) on the Earth, Earth's Moon, Jupiter and Venus.

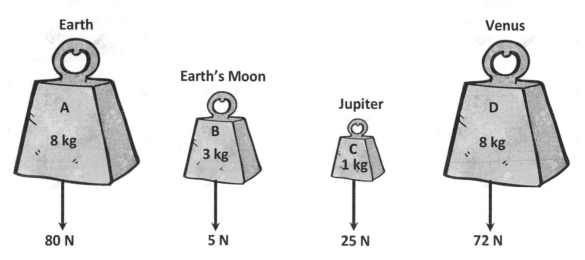

Earth

A

8 kg

80 N

Earth's Moon

B

3 kg

5 N

Jupiter

C

1 kg

25 N

Venus

D

8 kg

72 N

Which object, **A**, **B**, **C** or **D**, has the smallest mass?

How can you tell that the force of gravity is less on Venus than it is on the Earth?

(g) During the Apollo 15 mission to the Moon in 1971, astronaut David Scott conducted the famous hammer and feather experiment.

The hammer and feather were dropped at the same time from the same height and hit the surface of the Moon at the same time.

A hammer falls much faster on Earth than it does on the Moon. Explain why.

2019

Acknowledgements

Images

Image on page 59:	State Examinations Commission
Images on page 60:	State Examinations Commission; thoughtco.com
Image on page 61:	printablediagram.com
Image on page 62:	State Examinations Commission
Images on page 63:	E.M. Unit, Royal Free Hospital School of Medicine/Wellcome Trust Photo Library; State Examinations Commission
Image on page 64:	State Examinations Commission
Image on page 65:	State Examinations Commission
Image on page 66:	cottagelife.com
Image on page 67:	thoughtco.com
Images on page 68:	earthsky.org; State Examinations Commission
Images on page 70:	swastikchemicals.com; indiamart.com
Image on page 72:	State Examinations Commission
Images on page 73:	discountexplosion.com; bloginonline.com
Image on page 76:	newatlas.com
Image on page 77:	assignmentpoint.com
Image on page 78:	euchems.eu
Image on page 78:	State Examinations Commission
Images on page 80:	time.com; State Examinations Commission; timeanddate.com
Images on page 81:	moon.nasa.gov; State Examinations Commission
Images on page 82:	State Examinations Commission; hq.nasa.gov

Texts

Text on page 76:	Ring, Evelyn. *UCC study: High fibre foods ease stress effects*. Irish Examiner. <http://www.irishexaminer.com> (1 August 2018).

Material may have been adapted, for the purpose of assessment, without the authors' prior consent.

Junior Cycle Final Examination – Common Level

Science

Monday 10 June
Afternoon 2:00 – 4:00

Coimisiún na Scrúduithe Stáit
State Examinations Commission

Junior Cycle Final Examination
Sample Paper

Science

Common Level

Time: 2 hours

360 marks

Examination number

Centre stamp

SEC SAMPLE

Instructions

There are two sections in this examination paper.

Section A   150 marks   10 questions
Section B   210 marks   6 questions

Answer **all** parts of **all** questions.

You may ask the superintendent for a copy of the *Formulae and Tables* booklet. You must return it at the end of the examination. You are not allowed to bring your own copy into the examination.

Not all the questions carry equal marks. The number of marks for each question is stated at the top of the question.

You should spend about 50 minutes on Section A and 70 minutes on Section B.

Write your answers in the spaces provided in this booklet. You may lose marks if you do not do so. You are not required to use all of the space provided.

This examination booklet will be scanned and your work will be presented to an examiner on screen. Anything that you write outside of the answer areas may not be seen by the examiner.

You may only use blue or black pen when writing your answers. Do not use pencil.

There is extra space at the end of Section A and at the back of the booklet.
Label any extra work clearly with the question number and part.

Question 1   **15 marks**

All biological organisms are made up of cells.

(a)   Name the instrument shown in the picture on the right, which
        is used to examine cells.

(b)   Name the labelled part of the instrument, which makes the
        cells look bigger.

(c)   The picture below shows cells from an onion, which are typical plant cells.

        In the box, write the name of any one part of the cell.

        Draw an arrow from the box to the part of the cell you have named.

(d)   State the function of the part of the cell you have chosen.

Question 2   **15 marks**

Complete the table below for the instruments shown.

In each case, state what physical quantity the instrument measures.
Also state the unit used for that measurement.

(Some parts of the table are already completed for you.)

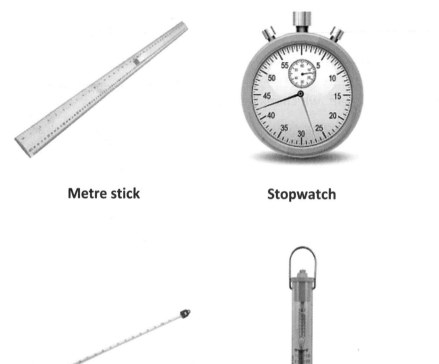

| Metre stick | Stopwatch | Graduated cylinder |

Thermometer   **Newton meter**   **Ohmmeter**

Instrument	Quantity measured	Unit
Metre stick		
Stopwatch		
Graduated cylinder		
Thermometer		
Newton meter		Newton (N)
Ohmmeter	Resistance	Ohm (Ω)

Question 3   **15 marks**

A group of students investigated how solubility in water changes with temperature for solid compounds **1**, **2** and **3**. The graph below shows the results obtained.

(a)   Hot water was needed during this investigation.

Name an instrument used to heat water in the laboratory.

(b)   Describe one safety precaution which should be taken when heating water in the laboratory.

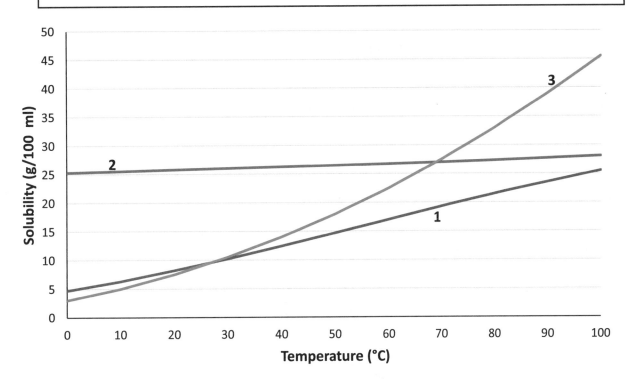

(c)   The general trend for solids is that solubility increases with temperature.

Which compound shows the greatest increase in solubility from 0 °C to 100 °C?

(d)   On the graph, circle the point where compound **2** has the same solubility as compound **3**.

(e)   State one advantage of presenting scientific data using a graph.

Question 4

The passage below explains how a cell gets the materials it needs for respiration.
The names of five parts of the body are missing from the passage.
Here are the missing body parts:

Heart   **Veins**   **Small intestine**   **Stomach**   **Lungs**

In the spaces provided, write the names of the missing body parts.

When we breathe we draw air into our _____ where the oxygen in the air is

passed into our blood.

After we swallow food it is first stored in our _____ for a few hours, where

some digestion occurs. Then it travels on to our _____ where further

digestion happens and glucose and other nutrients are absorbed into our blood.

Blood is pumped around the body by our _____ . The blood travels through

arteries and capillaries to all the cells in our body. The blood then travels back through

our _____ .

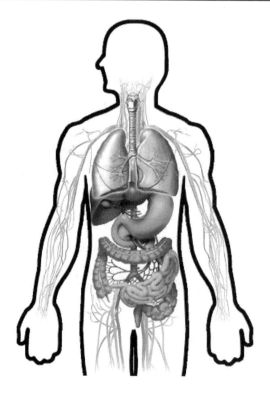

Question 5

15 marks

The diagram below shows some of the processes involved in the carbon cycle.

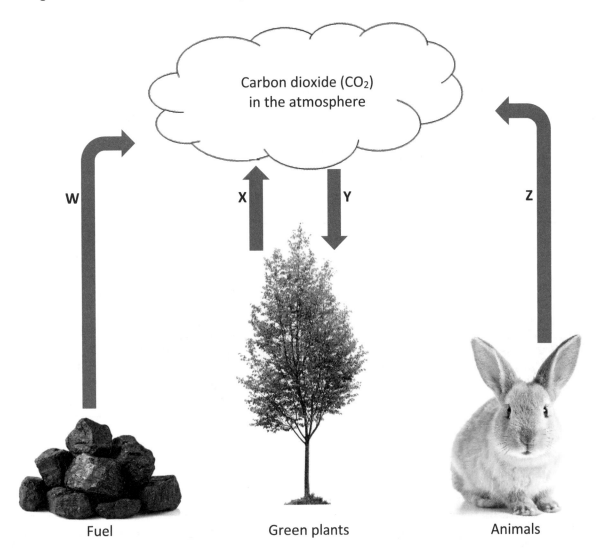

Each of the blue arrows **W**, **X**, **Y** and **Z** represents one of the following three processes:

Respiration   **Photosynthesis**   **Combustion**

In the table below, write the name of each process.
(Note that one process appears twice.)

Process	Name
W	
X	
Y	
Z	

Question 6   **15 marks**

In the diagrams below, circles of different colours are used to represent atoms of different elements.

Complete the table below for the substances shown in diagrams **A** to **E**.

In each case, state whether the diagram represents a solid, a liquid or a gas.

Also state whether the diagram represents an element, a compound or a mixture.

(Some parts of the table are already completed for you.)

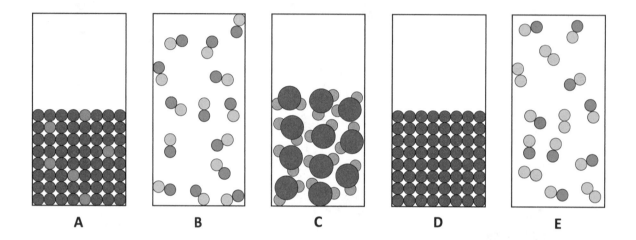

| A | B | C | D | E |

Diagram	Solid, liquid or gas	Element, compound or mixture
A		Mixture
B		
C		
D	Solid	
E		

Question 7   **15 marks**

The picture below shows a human female sex cell surrounded by human male sex cells.

Answer questions **(a)**, **(b)** and **(c)** by putting a tick (✓) in the correct box.
Tick one box only for each question.

(a)   What is the human female sex cell called?

   Sperm   ☐

   Egg   ☐

   Vagina   ☐

   Penis   ☐

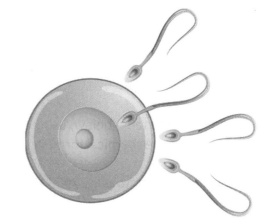

(b)   What is the human male sex cell called?

   Sperm   ☐

   Egg   ☐

   Vagina   ☐

   Penis   ☐

(c)   Where in the female reproductive system is the female sex cell produced?

   Womb   ☐

   Testes   ☐

   Vagina   ☐

   Ovary   ☐

(d)   In the diagram, draw a box around the male sex cell that is fertilising the female sex cell.

(e)   State one way of reducing the chance that sexual intercourse could result in fertilisation.

Question 8   **15 marks**

(a) Match each of the following sub-atomic particles to their descriptions in the table below.

Electron   Neutron   Proton

Description	Particle
Positively charged	
Negatively charged	
No charge	

(b) Complete the table below, using the Periodic Table of the elements to predict the ratio of atoms and the chemical formula for each of the compounds listed.

You should refer to page 79 of the *Formulae and Tables* booklet when answering this question.

The first row is completed for you.

Compound	First element	Second element	Ratio	Formula
Water	Hydrogen (H)	Oxygen (O)	2 : 1	H_2O
Magnesium chloride	Magnesium (Mg)	Chlorine (Cl)	:	
Ammonia	Nitrogen (N)	Hydrogen (H)	:	

Question 9   **15 marks**

A student investigated the relationship between the potential difference (voltage) across a resistor and the current flowing through it.

The circuit diagram below shows the arrangement of the apparatus used by the student.

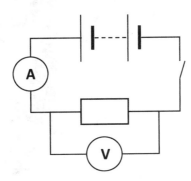

Examine the circuit diagram and answer the questions below.

(a)   The instrument labelled **V** measures voltage. Name instrument **V**.

(b)   The instrument labelled **A** measures current. Name instrument **A**.

(c)   In the circuit diagram above, draw a circle around the symbol for the switch.

(d)   The student found that current is proportional to voltage for this resistor.
      Using the axes provided, draw a sketch of a graph to show this relationship.

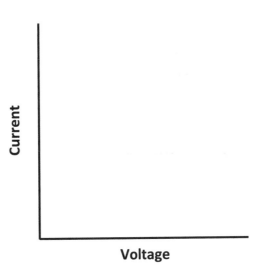

Question 10

Read the following article, taken from an online newspaper, and answer the questions that follow.

Space invaders: the alien species that are costing us millions

In 1847 the Japanese knotweed was a medal-winning plant with strong growth and pretty white flowers. Things are very different today, with British house buyers being denied mortgages if this plant is found on a property.

It has also taken hold in Ireland. Japanese knotweed can grow through the smallest crack and grow up to 2 cm a day, extending 7 m horizontally and 3 m deep. It is one of a number of unwanted and sometimes dangerous invasive species that have taken foothold in Ireland.

Invasive species are often present due to human intervention. Some species have been deliberately released, while others, such as the American mink and the giant rhubarb, have escaped from farms and gardens. Others, such as the New Zealand flatworm, arrived accidentally in the soil of imported plants.

Some invasive plants such as the Japanese knotweed die back during winter, exposing the soil and leading to erosion.

irishtimes.com

(a) Name one invasive species found in Ireland.

(b) Describe one way an invasive species could get to Ireland.

(c) In the comments section below this article, an online reader comments that "all species are invasive – that's nature, that's evolution".

Do you agree or disagree with this comment? Explain your answer.

Additional writing space for **Section A**.
Label all work clearly with the question number and part.

Question 11   **30 marks**

Citric acid is a chemical found in lemons and some other fruits.

It is a white crystalline solid when pure.

Solid citric acid may be dissolved in water to make a citric acid solution.

(a)   Describe how to make up a solution which contains 5 g of citric acid dissolved in 100 ml of water. As part of your description, name each piece of equipment you would use.
      (A labelled diagram may help your answer.)

	Labelled diagram

Baking soda is another white solid compound. Its chemical name is sodium hydrogen carbonate. It is often used in making bread and cake.

When baking soda is added to a test tube of citric acid solution, fizzing occurs and a gas is produced.

(b) A student holding the test tube notices that it cools down during the reaction.

Is this reaction an example of an endothermic or an exothermic reaction? Explain your answer.

This reaction is also an example of an acid-base reaction.

When baking soda is added to a test tube of citric acid solution, the chemicals react and the pH of the solution changes.

(c) Would you expect the pH of the solution in the test tube to increase or decrease during the reaction? Explain your answer.

(d) Describe how you could investigate how pH changes during the reaction.

Question 12

Sankey diagrams are named after H. Riall Sankey, a Tipperary-born engineer, following his 1898 description of the energy efficiency of a steam engine.

Sankey diagrams show the flow of energy to and from a device.

In a Sankey diagram, the width of each arrow represents the proportion of energy named.

The Sankey diagrams for a filament lamp and a compact fluorescent lamp (CFL) are shown below.

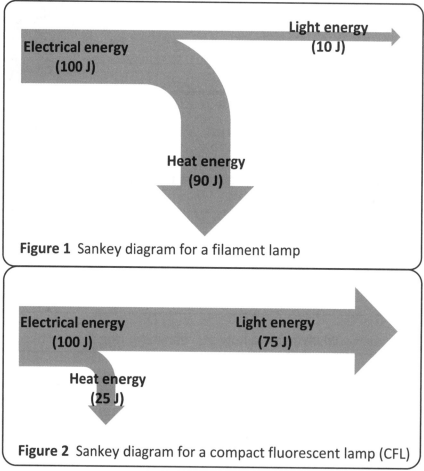

Figure 1 Sankey diagram for a filament lamp

Figure 2 Sankey diagram for a compact fluorescent lamp (CFL)

(a) Examine figures **1** and **2**. Which lamp is more efficient? Justify your answer.

(b) Why is it important to improve the energy efficiency of household devices, such as lamps?

(c) A student is asked to investigate and compare the heat energy produced by filament lamps and CFLs.

Apart from the lamps themselves, name a piece of equipment that could be used during this investigation. Explain how this piece of equipment could be used during the investigation.

(d) The energy conversions that happen in a CFL are described in the table below.
Complete the table for another device which transforms energy from one form to another and which you designed as part of your studies in science.

Name of the device	Function of the device	Main useful energy conversion	Main loss of energy
Compact fluorescent lamp (CFL)	To provide artificial light	Electrical to light	Electrical to heat

(e) Sketch a Sankey diagram for the device you described in part **(d)**.
Label each part of the diagram.

Labelled Sankey diagram

fcknms
Visit www.e-xamit.ie

Question 13

Solar eclipses can happen a few times each year.

(a) The diagram below shows a simple model of a solar eclipse (an eclipse of the Sun). In the diagram, write the letter **X** for Earth, **Y** for Moon and **Z** for Sun.

(b) Two weeks before or after a solar eclipse sometimes there is a lunar eclipse (an eclipse of the Moon). Draw a labelled diagram to show a model of a lunar eclipse.

Labelled diagram

A solar eclipse in March 2015 affected the solar electrical power produced in the German electricity grid.

The graph below shows the solar electrical power produced from Monday to Friday during the week of the solar eclipse.

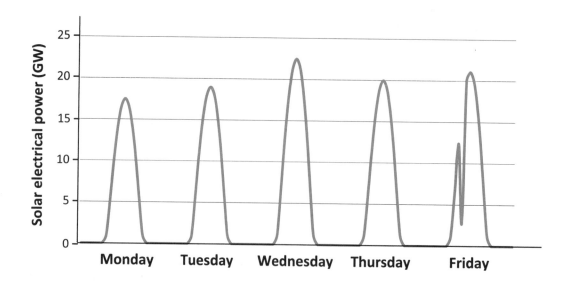

(c) On which day of the week did the solar eclipse occur? Justify your answer.

(d) Which was the brightest day of the week? Justify your answer.

(e)

The Sun can also provide power for modern spacecraft. The Juno mission to Jupiter uses solar energy to produce electricity.

Previous long-distance space missions used nuclear power to produce electricity.

State one advantage of using solar energy rather than nuclear energy during space exploration.

(f) JunoCam, a camera on the Juno probe, is powered by Juno's solar panels.

Calculate the electrical power (P) generated by JunoCam when it uses a current of 0.5 A flowing across a potential difference (voltage) of 12 V.

Calculation

Question 14

A group of students carried out a habitat study.

(a) Use some of the words in the list to name the pieces of equipment shown below, which can be used in a habitat study.

Beating tray   **Pooter**   **Net**   **Pitfall trap**

Picture	Name

(b) The students also used a quadrat during their habitat study.

What shape is a quadrat? Describe how the students might have used the quadrat.

In one part of the habitat, the students used the quadrat 30 times and found that a certain species was present on 18 occasions. Calculate the percentage frequency of that species.

Calculation

The students were given permission to remove some green plants from the habitat to take back to their school laboratory. They did this in order to investigate factors that affect photosynthesis.

(c) Imagine that you are one of the students. You have been asked to carry out an experiment to investigate how any one factor affects photosynthesis.

Name one factor which could affect photosynthesis and which you might investigate.

List two factors which you would keep constant (fixed) during the experiment to ensure that it is a fair test.

(d) Write a suitable hypothesis for this experiment.

(e) Draw a labelled diagram of the setup of your experiment.

Labelled diagram

Question 15

Some chemical reactions proceed quickly while some proceed at a slower rate.

During your studies, you investigated the effect of a number of variables on the rate of production of a common gas.

(a)   Name a common gas that could be produced in the laboratory.

(b)   Draw a labelled diagram of how this gas could be produced.
Include labels for any equipment and chemicals used.

Labelled diagram

(c)   Explain how you tested this gas to confirm its identity.
Include the result of the test.

A student carried out an experiment to investigate the effect of temperature on the rate of production of a certain gas. The first reaction happened at 20 °C and the second one at 30 °C.

In both cases the gas produced was passed through water as it was collected. This was to ensure that the gas was always at room temperature (a constant) when its volume was measured.

The student recorded the following results:

Time (s)	Volume of gas (cm³) for reaction at 20 °C	Volume of gas (cm³) for reaction at 30 °C
0	0	0
30	7	10
60	13	16
90	17	19
120	19	20
150	20	20

(d) In the space below, draw graphs for both sets of results.

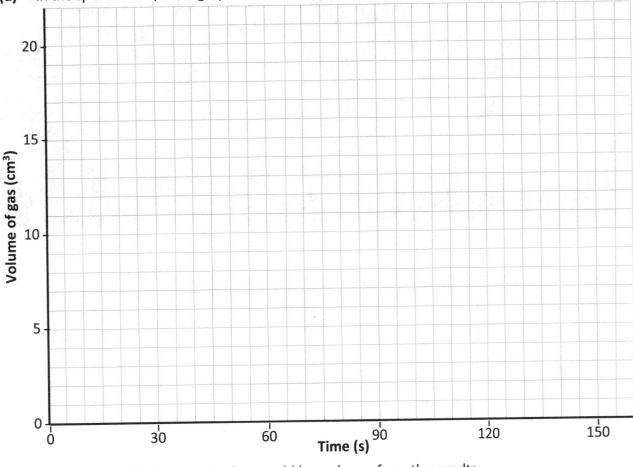

(e) State two conclusions the student could have drawn from the results.

Question 16

The planet Jupiter is the largest planet in our solar system and is described as a "gas giant". Jupiter has four large moons and many smaller ones.

These large moons were discovered in 1610 by Italian scientist Galileo Galilei.

Data about the size and density of the four large moons of Jupiter are given in the table below.

Moon of Jupiter	Diameter (km)	Density (g/cm³)
Io	3640	3.53
Europa	3120	3.01
Ganymede	5270	1.94
Callisto	4820	1.83

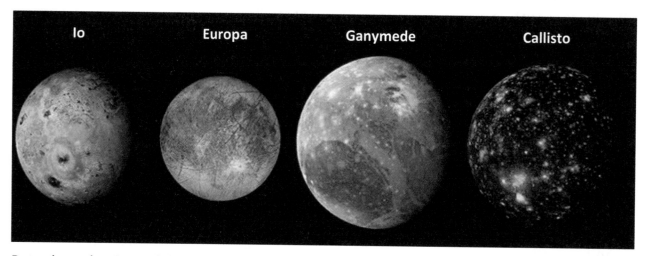

Data about the size and density of some other objects in our solar system are given in the table below.

Object	Diameter (km)	Density (g/cm³)
Mercury	4880	5.43
Earth	12700	5.51
Earth's Moon	3470	3.34
Mars	6780	3.93
Jupiter	140000	1.33
The Sun	139000000	1.41

The densities of four materials commonly found in planets and moons are given in the table on the right.

Material	Density (g/cm³)
Water	1.0
Granite	2.8
Basalt	3.0
Iron	8.0

(a) A solid of mass 12 g has a volume of 1.5 cm³.

Calculate the density of the material.
Hence identify the material as either water, granite, basalt or iron.

Calculation

Material: _____

(b) Granite and basalt are found in the Earth's crust. Use the data given in the tables to state whether or not it is likely that all of the Earth is made of these rocks. Justify your answer.

(c) Use the data given for Jupiter and Earth to explain why Jupiter is described as a "gas giant".

(d) Callisto is a moon and Mercury, of similar size, is a planet.
What is the difference between a moon and a planet?

(e) Galileo's discovery of the moons of Jupiter changed our understanding of Earth and space. Describe another example of how our scientific understanding changed over time.

(f) Scientists estimate that our solar system began to form about 4.6 billion years ago. Scientists also estimate that our universe formed 13.8 billion years ago.

Describe two things that scientists believe happened during the early formation of the universe – before the formation of solar systems.

Additional writing space for **Section B**.
Label all work clearly with the question number and part.

Acknowledgements

Images

Images on page 87: homesciencetools.com; microbehunter.com
Images on page 88: amazon.co.uk; apps.garmin.com; stemcelltulsa.com; willtronics.com.au; phillipharris.co.uk; indiamart.com
Image on page 89: State Examinations Commission
Image on page 90: microbemagic.ucc.ie
Images on page 91: couriermail.com.au; pixels.com; rabbits.life
Images on page 92: State Examinations Commission
Image on page 93: vectorstock.com
Image on page 96: strainkeville.co.uk
Image on page 98: thespruce.com
Image on page 99: classroomclipart.com
Images on page 100: gracesguide.co.uk; State Examinations Commission
Images on page 102: State Examinations Commission
Images on page 103: gizmondo.com; petapixel.com
Images on page 104: openi.nlm.nih.gov; handsontheland.org
Image on page 106: classroomclipart.com
Image on page 108: forcetoknow.com

Texts

Text on page 96: Nesbitt, Jill. *Space invaders: the alien species that are costing us millions*. <http://www.irishtimes.com/news/science> (5 March 2018).

Junior Cycle Final Examination – Common Level

Science

Sample Paper
Time: 2 hours

2019J057C1E2828S

Junior Cycle 20XX
Final Examination
Sample Paper A

Science

Common Level

Time: 2 hours

June – Morning 9:30 to 11:30

360 marks

Examination number				

Instructions

There are two sections in this examination paper.

Section A $\qquad$ 150 marks $\quad$ 10 questions
Section B $\qquad$ 210 marks $\quad$ 5 questions

Answer **all** parts of **all** questions.

You may ask the superintendent for a copy of the *Formulae and Tables* booklet. You must return it at the end of the examination. You are not allowed to bring your own copy into the examination.

Not all the questions carry equal marks. The number of marks for each question is stated at the top of the question.

You should spend about 50 minutes on Section A and 70 minutes on Section B.

Write your answers in the spaces provided in this booklet. You may lose marks if you do not do so. You are not required to use all of the space provided.

This examination booklet will be scanned and your work will be presented to an examiner on screen. Anything that you write outside of the answer areas may not be seen by the examiner.

You may only use blue or black pen when writing your answers. Do not use pencil.

There is extra space at the end of Section A and at the back of the booklet.
Label any extra work clearly with the question number and part.

Question 1   **15 marks**

The diagram below represents the human digestive system.

Examine the diagram and answer the questions that follow.

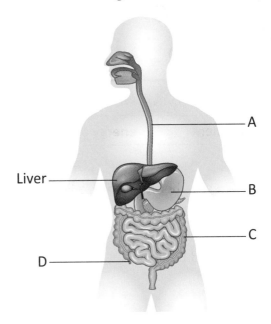

(a)   In the table write the name of the parts labelled B and D.

Label	Name of part
B	
D	

(b)   In what labelled part would you expect to find hydrochloric acid?

_____

(c)   Digestion is the breakdown of food. Digestion can be physical or chemical. Name the chemicals responsible for chemical digestion.

_____

(d)   Fibre is a carbohydrate that forms an important part of our diet. What is the function of fibre in our diet?

_____

_____

ogfmcx
Visit www.e-xamit.ie

Question 2

Matter has three forms, which are known as the three states of matter. From the following list of words, complete the passage below.

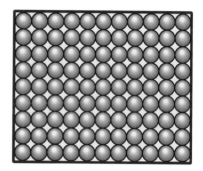 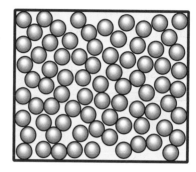 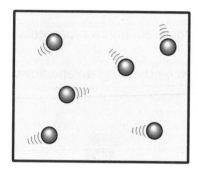

move	tightly	same	arrangement	energy

The particles in a substance stay the _____ whether it's a solid, a liquid or a gas.

What changes is the _____ of the particles and their

_____ .

In solids, particles are held _____ together.

In liquids and gases, the particles can _____ so they can change shape.

vmutxc
Visit www.e-xamit.ie

116

Question 3   **15 marks**

The picture illustrates a visual comparison between Earth and Uranus. Using the data given in the table answer the following questions.

Comparison information	Earth	Uranus
Average distance from the sun	149.6 million kilometres	2.871 billion kilometres
Average temperature	20 degrees Celsius	−224 degrees Celsius
Gravity	1	0.89
Atmosphere	Oxygen, carbon dioxide, nitrogen	Hydrogen, helium

(a) From the above data, could life exist on Uranus?

_____

(b) Justify your answer.

_____

_____

_____

(c) Looking at the temperature of both planets, analyse how the distance from the sun affects the surface temperature. Refer to both sets of data in your answer.

_____

_____

_____

_____

ccpvwl
Visit www.e-xamit.ie

Question 4   **15 marks**

Consider what might happen when a match is ignited and burning.

(a)   Is this a physical change or a chemical change?

_____

_____

(b)   Name the **two** types of energy released.

1. _____

2. _____

(c)   Explain why this change cannot be reversed.

_____

_____

_____

(d)   Name the **two** gases produced as this match is burning.

1. _____

2. _____

Question 5   15 marks

Complete the table below for the instruments shown.

In each case, state a physical quantity the instrument measures.

Also state the unit used for a measurement.

(Some parts of the table are already completed for you.)

Trundle wheel      **Analogue ammeter**

Vernier calipers      **Analogue voltmeter**

Balance      **Digital multimeter**

Instrument	Quantity measured	Unit
Trundle wheel		
Vernier calipers		
Balance	Mass	
Analogue ammeter		
Analogue voltmeter	Potential difference	Volt (V)
Digital multimeter		

Question 6 15 marks

Use this table to help you answer questions about the elements listed in the table below.

Element	Atomic number	Mass number
Oxygen	8	16
Chlorine	17	35
Gallium	31	70
Zinc	30	68
Tungsten	74	184

(a)   State the number of protons in an atom of chlorine.

_____

(b)   Identify the structure within an atom where the protons are found.

_____

(c)   State the number of neutrons in an atom of zinc.

_____

(d)   Identify the location of the electrons in an atom.

_____

(e)   State the element in the table above which has the same number of protons and neutrons.

_____

bbfbsp
Visit www.e-xamit.ie

120

Question 7   **15 marks**

The passage below explains how plants carry out photosynthesis. The names of five substances are missing from the passage.

The missing substances are:

water   **oxygen**   **chlorophyll**   **carbon dioxide**   **glucose**

Write the name of each substance into the correct space in the passage.

A green leaf absorbs _____ gas from the air.

It combines this gas with _____ absorbed from the soil.

The products of photosynthesis are _____ gas and the carbohydrate

_____ .

Photosynthesis is the conversion of solar energy into chemical energy. The catalyst that speeds up

this conversion is called _____ .

Latte Levy could reduce disposable coffee cups by 250,000 a day

Around a quarter of a million disposable coffee cups could be diverted from Irish landfill every day if a 15-cent levy on cups was introduced alongside other environmentally friendly measures, a new piece of research indicates.

The research published on Monday suggests a 'Latte Levy' on its own would see the amount of takeaway cups thrown away daily by Irish consumers fall by 70,000 while the number would increase by more than 300 per cent if combined with other positive behavioural nudges, including discounts for using reusable mugs, being given a free reusable cup or a refund for returning a plastic cup.

The research said that on average Irish adults drink four hot drinks a week, with around two million plastic cups sold every day. Few of the cups are recyclable.

The Government has proposed a new 15-cent levy on most disposable coffee cups to incentivise the use of reusable cups.

(a)   On average how many plastic cups are sold in Ireland every day?

_____

_____

_____

(b)   Why have the Irish Government proposed a new 15-cent levy on most disposable cups?

_____

_____

_____

(c)   In your opinion, will this Latte Levy incentivise the use of reusable cups?

_____

_____

_____

_____

fboyke
Visit www.e-xamit.ie

Question 9

Speed limits on roads use the kilometre per hour (km h⁻¹), but in science we often express speed in metres per second (m s⁻¹). Sometimes we need to change units.

(a) Convert 2 hours to seconds.

_____

(b) Convert 3.8 km to metres (m) and then to centimetres (cm).

_____

_____

(c) To calculate speed we use the following equation: $\text{speed} = \dfrac{\text{distance}}{\text{time}}$

A car travels 144 kilometres in 2 hours.

  (i) Calculate the speed of the car in kilometres per hour.

Calculation

  (ii) By changing the 144 kilometres to metres and the 2 hours to seconds, calculate the speed of the car in metres per second.

Calculation

Edco SAMPLE A

Question 10

Match the following definitions to the correct word.

An object that orbits the sun	galaxy
A collection of billions of stars	star
An object composed of frozen gases, rocks and dust	moon
Nuclear reactions take place here	sun
Formed the same time as the solar system	comet
Main sequence star	planet

dchgth
Visit www.e-xamit.ie

124

Additional writing space for **Section A**.
Label all work clearly with the question number and part.

Question 11

30 marks

Investigate how the amount of light affects the rate of photosynthesis. They used a plant called pondweed, which grows under water. The apparatus used is shown in the diagram below.

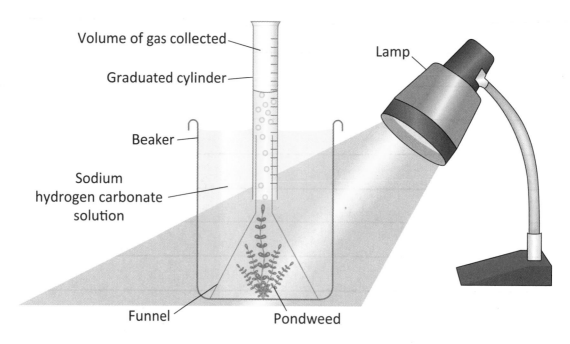

(a) Name the gas collected in the graduated cylinder.

_____

_____

(b) Sodium hydrogen carbonate is water soluble and releases carbon dioxide.

Suggest why sodium hydrogen carbonate was necessary in this investigation.

_____

_____

_____

(c) What would you expect to happen to the volume of gas produced if the pondweed were left in the dark? Explain your answer.

_____

_____

_____

(d) The table below shows the volume of gas collected over the course of 60 minutes.

Time (minutes)	10	20	30	40	50	60
Total volume of gas collected (cm³)	4.0	12.0	24.0	28.0	29.0	30.0

Use the information in the table above to draw a graph of the results obtained.

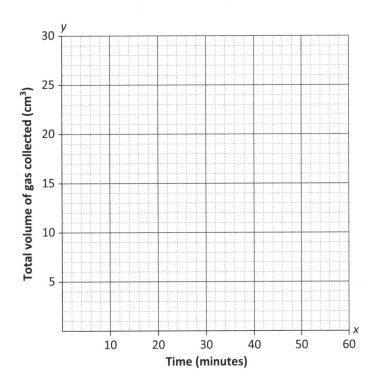

(e) From the graph calculate how much gas was collected after 15 minutes.

Calculation

(f) Suggest how the student might have reduced the amount of light the pondweed received.

_____

_____

What effect would you expect a reduction in the amount of light to have on the volumes of gas collected?

_____

_____

Question 12 **30 marks**

A student performs an activity to investigate the relationship between mass and volume. She obtains five pieces of brass and measures and records their mass and volume.

The recorded data are given below.

Mass (g)	Volume (cm³)	Density ( )
100	12	8.33
200	23.5	
300	35	
400	47	
500	59	

(a) Name the instrument used to measure the mass values.

_____

(b) Name **one** piece of equipment used to measure the volume of the brass pieces.

_____

(c) The student, while researching online, reads that if the mass is divided by the volume a new value called density is obtained. Mathematically:

$$density = \frac{mass}{volume}$$

She tries this for the first pair of values, as can be seen in the data table above, and obtains a value of 8.33.

Repeat this calculation for the other **four** pairs of values. Clearly show your work in the space below.

Fill in the four blank spaces in the data table above.

Calculation

(d) The unit for density was omitted in the data table. Using the fact that:

$$\text{density} = \frac{\text{mass}}{\text{volume}}$$

write the unit for density in the space below.

_____

_____

(e) 64 sugar cubes were stacked neatly to form a larger cube that measured 4 cm long, 4 cm wide and 4 cm high. Each individual cube had a volume of 1 cm³. The volume of the 64 sugar cubes was therefore 64 cm³. The mass of the 64 sugar cubes was measured as 144 g.

The cubes were broken up into smaller grains. The mass of the sugar remained the same, but the volume appeared to increase. Explain why in the space below. Include a diagram as part of your explanation.

_____

_____

_____

_____

Question 13 45 marks

Two bottles were knocked over in a chemistry storeroom. One powder was silver nitrate (soluble in water) and the other was silver chloride (insoluble in water). A student carefully removed the broken glass and recovered a mixture of the two powders.

(a) Explain the terms soluble and insoluble.

Soluble: _____

Insoluble: _____

(b) The student then added water to the mixture of powders. Explain why.

_____

(c) The next step in the process was filtration. Draw a labelled diagram and describe in detail how she did this. As part of your description, name each piece of equipment she would have used.

(d) Name the residue and filtrate.

Residue: _____

Filtrate: _____

(e) The final step was evaporation. Describe how the student carried this out.

_____

_____

_____

_____

Question 14

(a) The Earth and the Moon orbit around the Sun. At times during their orbit they can get in the way of each other. When this happens, we call the event an eclipse.

In the space provided below, draw the position of the Sun, Earth and Moon during:

(i) A lunar eclipse

(ii) A solar eclipse

(b) On Earth we experience a lunar eclipse more often than a solar eclipse.

Based on your knowledge of the lunar phases and the position of the Moon, explain the statement above.

_____

_____

_____

_____

(c)

Looking at the picture above, explain why humans need to wear eye protection when viewing a solar eclipse but do not need eye protection for a lunar eclipse.

Lunar eclipse: _____

_____

Solar eclipse: _____

_____

(d) Match the statements to the correct word from this list:

Umbra   Penumbra   Totality

Partial darkened shadow	
Area is in complete darkness	
Area is in complete dark shadow	

(e) The moon rotates around the Earth once every 27 days. Explain why we do not experience a lunar eclipse on Earth every month as a result.

_____

_____

_____

_____

Question 15   **60 marks**

A student performed an activity
to investigate the relationship
between the extension of a spring
and the applied force. The force
was applied by hanging weights
from the spring.

The value of each weight in newtons was stamped on it. The student recorded the value of all the
weights.

The extension of the spring was measured using a metre stick. The extension was measured in cm.
The student recorded the value of the extension for each of the applied forces.

The data recorded are given in the table below.

Applied force (N)	Extension (cm)
5	2
10	4
15	6
20	8
25	10
30	12

(a) Name the instrument that is used to measure weight.

_____

(b) Draw a labelled diagram of the equipment that the student used.

(c) In the space below, draw a graph of the recorded data.

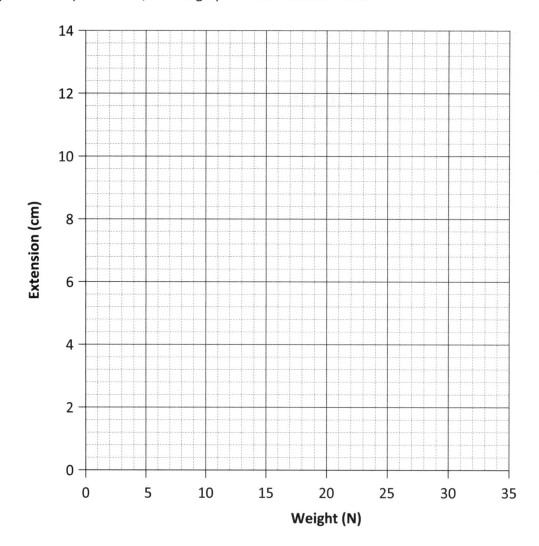

(d) From the graph determine which weight would cause an extension of 9 cm. Write your answer below.

_____

(e) From the graph determine the extension that would be caused by 8 N. Write your answer below.

_____

(f) Suggest a possible outcome if the student were to continue the investigation using heavier weights.

_____

_____

_____

Additional writing space for **Section B**.
Label all work clearly with the question number and part.

Edco
SAMPLE A

Additional writing space for **Section B**.
Label all work clearly with the question number and part.

Junior Cycle 20XX
Final Examination
Sample Paper B

Science

Common Level

Time: 2 hours

June – Morning 9:30 to 11:30

360 marks

Examination number				

Instructions

There are two sections in this examination paper.

Section A   150 marks   10 questions
Section B   210 marks   5 questions

Answer **all** parts of **all** questions.

You may ask the superintendent for a copy of the *Formulae and Tables* booklet. You must return it at the end of the examination. You are not allowed to bring your own copy into the examination.

Not all the questions carry equal marks. The number of marks for each question is stated at the top of the question.

You should spend about 50 minutes on Section A and 70 minutes on Section B.

Write your answers in the spaces provided in this booklet. You may lose marks if you do not do so. You are not required to use all of the space provided.

This examination booklet will be scanned and your work will be presented to an examiner on screen. Anything that you write outside of the answer areas may not be seen by the examiner.

You may only use blue or black pen when writing your answers. Do not use pencil.

There is extra space at the end of Section A and at the back of the booklet.
Label any extra work clearly with the question number and part.

Section A

150 Marks

Question 1

15 marks

Complete the following paragraph on stars, using words from the list below:

red giant   sequence   fuse   stable   expand   luminous

nuclear   hydrogen   phases   gravity   heat   nebulae

galaxy   energy   white dwarf

A star is a _____ object that can produce its own light and _____ from

_____ reactions. These reactions take place when two _____ atoms

_____ to produce helium. There are many _____ in the life cycle of a

star. The formation of a star occurs when _____ between gas particles in large gas

clouds, called _____ , causes the clouds to collapse and come together.

Our sun is called a main _____ star and is in its _____ period.

When a star has used up all its supplies at its core it begins using helium in its outer parts,

causing the star to _____ and release more heat. This structure is called a

_____ _____ .

Question 2

15 marks

The rate of a chemical reaction tells us how quickly a chemical reaction takes place. Use the following words to complete the passage.

surface area   **temperature**   **energy**   **collisions**   **number**

Increasing the rate of a reaction involves increasing the _____ of successful

_____ between particles. For the particles to react they must collide with enough

_____ to break bonds in the molecule. There are four factors which can change the

rate of a reaction: concentration, _____, suitable catalyst and _____

_____ .

Question 3

The picture below is an illustration of our solar system. Using the list of planets given, place them in the correct order, starting from the sun and moving outwards.

Neptune, Earth, Saturn, Pluto, Mercury, Jupiter, Venus, Uranus, Mars

Sun

Question 4   **15 marks**

Look at the periodic table below.

Select the letters which represent the following:

(a)   An element with a full outer shell

(b)   An alkali metal in period 3

(c)   An element with four shells

(d)   A halogen in period 3

(e)   An element that must be stored in oil.

Question 5

Blood is composed of plasma, red blood cells, white blood cells and platelets.

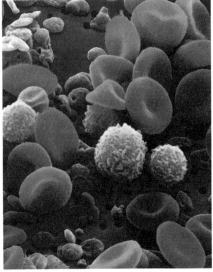

(a) Connect the parts of the blood with their functions below (one of the connections has already been completed).

Parts
Plasma
Red cells
White cells
Platelets

Functions
Form blood clots
Fight infections
Transports materials and heat
Carry oxygen

(b) Four blood vessels, labelled **A**, **B**, **C** and **D**, are attached to the heart.

Complete the table below by inserting the correct letter.

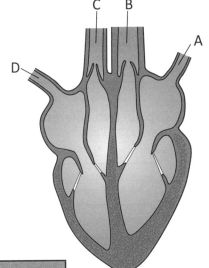

Description	Part
Carries blood all around the body	
Transports low oxygen blood into the heart	
Carries blood from the lungs to the heart	
Takes blood to the lungs	

Edco SAMPLE B

Question 6

15 marks

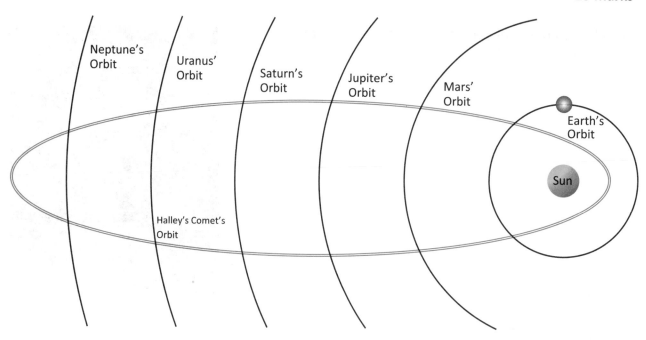

The above illustration shows a 'short period' comet which is named after English astronomer Edmond Halley. Halley examined reports of a comet approaching Earth in 1531, 1607 and 1682. He concluded that these three comets were actually the same comet returning again and again and predicted that the comet would come again in 1758. The last appearance of Halley's comet, as seen from Earth, was 1986.

Answer the following questions in relation to the above information.

(a) Calculate when Halley's comet will next be seen from Earth.

_____

(b) Explain **two** differences between a comet and a planet.

1. _____

2. _____

(c) Describe, in your own words, what your understanding is of the term 'short period' comet.

_____

_____

Question 7   **15 marks**

A biologist studied a marine (ocean) ecosystem and identified the following food chain.

Food chain

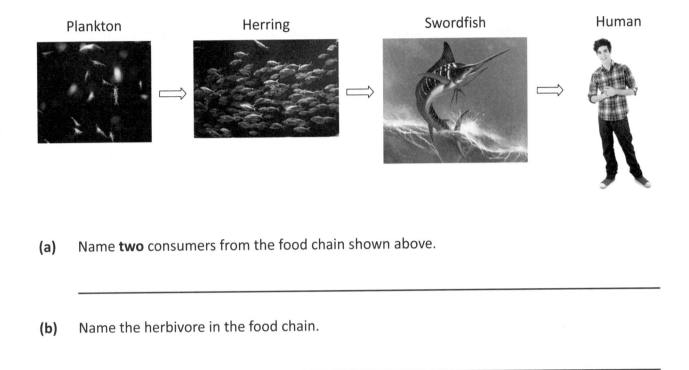

Plankton   Herring   Swordfish   Human

(a)   Name **two** consumers from the food chain shown above.

_____

(b)   Name the herbivore in the food chain.

_____

(c)   The plankton act as producers in this food chain. What does this mean?

_____

_____

(d)   After the biologist had finished her research a disease killed all the herrings in the ecosystem. Place an X in one of the following boxes to indicate what effect (if any) this might have on the number of swordfish.

The number of swordfish would stay the same.   ☐

The number of swordfish would decrease.   ☐

The number of swordfish would increase.   ☐

Question 8   **15 marks**

The passage below is about measurements that are used in everyday life and in science.

Fill in the spaces using the words given below.

area   mass   distance   seconds   metres cubed (m³)

Measuring is a skill that you need to practise in order to be good at science. However, we also

use measurements in our everyday lives. The time taken to travel to school, which we measure

in minutes, depends on the distance from home to school, which is measured in kilometres.

In science we measure time in _____ and _____

in metres.

We often measure the volume of water we drink in litres. In science we measure volume in

centimetres cubed (cm³) or in _____ .

The size or _____ of a classroom or a room in our home would be

measured in metres squared (m²), which is also the unit used in science.

Many food items are sold according to their _____ , measured in grams or

kilograms, which are also the units used in science.

146

How Ireland's plastic pollution became part of our diet

Plastics are entering the world's oceans at an alarming rate and Irish scientists are finding them everywhere, from deep-sea sediments and arctic ice, to the stomachs of marine mammals, birds and even fish that end up on our dinner plates.

'We know that they're in the human food chain because they're in fish,' says Dr Anne Marie Mahon of the Marine and Freshwater Research Centre at the Galway-Mayo Institute of Technology. 'We know that plastics contain endocrine disruptors, which can be carcinogenic, so yeah, this is really of concern.'

Scientists already know plastic pollution is dangerous and even deadly for marine animals, but the human health implications are still unknown.

The amount of plastic waste created in Ireland is also unknown, as the EPA is only obliged to report on plastic packaging waste; microplastic waste created by a range of industries is currently not measured or regulated. Microplastics are so small, less than 5 mm in diameter, and they escape the filters of most waste water treatment plants.

'90 per cent of microplastics channelled through the waste water treatment system is ending up in the sewage sludge and 10 per cent is still going out in our treated water, which then goes back into our rivers and our lakes,' explains Mahon. 'We actually apply our sewage sludge mostly to agricultural land for tillage and we don't know or understand what happens to it after that.'

Edco SAMPLE B

(a)   Name **one** place where Irish scientists are finding plastics in our ocean.

_____

(b)   Explain why scientists believe that plastics are in the human food chain.

_____

_____

_____

(c)   We can all contribute to reducing the plastic pollution in our oceans by following the three Rs – reduce, reuse, recycle.

Explain the statement above.

_____

_____

_____

_____

_____

Question 10

15 marks

(a) A student is measuring the length of a page in a copybook.

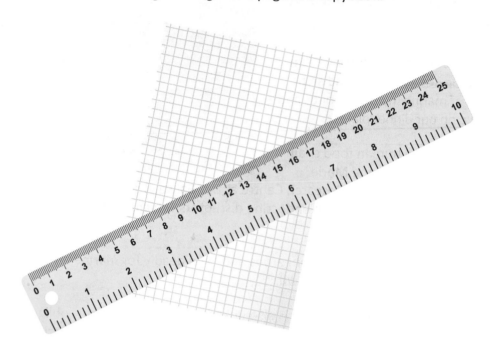

If the student does not realise the end of the ruler is not the zero mark, an error will be made. Name this type of error.

_____

The length of the page is 30 cm and the width of the page is 200 mm. Calculate the area of the page in centimetres squared (cm²).

_____

_____

(b) A student is measuring the perimeter of a tennis court and wants to use an instrument from the science laboratory. Which of the following would they use?

Metre stick   **Trundle wheel**   **Opisometer**

_____

Name **one** instrument from the above list they would not use and explain why.

_____

_____

Additional writing space for **Section A**.
Label all work clearly with the question number and part.

Question 11 | **30 marks**

The leaves below are as they appear in the autumn.

Leaves are green during the summer but in autumn they are red, orange and yellow. The leaves change colour because of chemical reactions. A group of students decided to investigate what changes occur during these chemical reactions. They conducted the following activity.

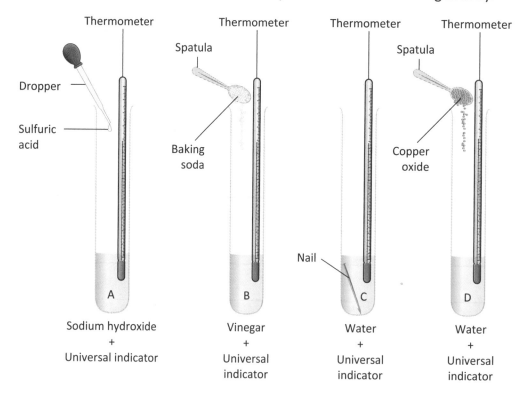

Universal indicator shows, by means of a colour change, whether a substance is an acid, a base or neutral.

(a) State the colour of universal indicator in each test tube and say whether it is acid, base or neutral.

Test tube	Solution	Colour of indicator	Acid/base/neutral
A	Sodium hydroxide		
B	Vinegar		
C	Water		
D	Water		

(b) In which test tube do you expect the universal indicator to change colour during the chemical reaction? Explain your answer.

_____

_____

_____

(c) When baking soda was added to vinegar in test tube **B**, fizzing occurred as carbon dioxide gas was produced. Describe a test that the students could carry out to prove this gas is carbon dioxide.

_____

_____

_____

_____

(d) The thermometer in test tube **A** and **B** showed a slight increase in temperature. Is this reaction endothermic or exothermic? Explain your answer.

_____

_____

_____

(e) During a chemical reaction the atoms rearrange to form a new substance. Outline the signs that indicate this may have occurred during the investigation.

_____

_____

_____

Question 12 **30 marks**

Two students, Shane and Alison, measured their breathing rate a number of times at rest. They then measured their breathing rate after they exercised until the rates returned to their resting rates.

The results are shown in the table below.

	Breaths per minute at rest	Breaths per minute after exercise				
Shane	10, 8, 12	24	16	10		
Alison	12, 14, 10	30	22	18	14	12

(a) Calculate the average resting rate per minute for both Shane and Alison. Show your calculations in the box below.

> Calculation

Shane's average breathing rate at rest	
Alison's average breathing rate at rest	

(b) Calculate the length of time it took the breathing rate of each student to return to normal and enter your answers below.

Number of minutes for Shane to recover	
Number of minutes for Alison to recover	

(c) Explain why our breathing rate increases after exercise.

_____

_____

_____

_____

_____

(d) Would you expect heart rate to increase after exercise? Explain your answer.

_____

_____

_____

_____

_____

(e) One of the two students admitted to smoking cigarettes on a regular basis. Which student do you suspect was the smoker? Give **two** reasons in support of your answer.

_____

_____

_____

_____

_____

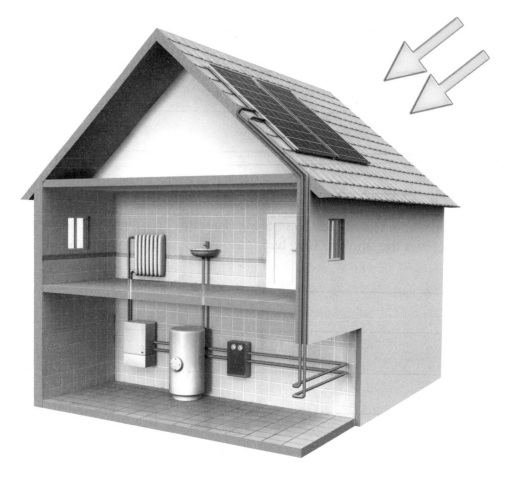

(a) What energy transformation is being illustrated in the photo above?

_____

_____

_____

_____

(b) What is the benefit of the energy transformation shown in the photo above?

_____

_____

_____

_____

(c) Comment on why it might be unwise to rely totally on the method shown in the photo on the previous page for a hot water system.

_____

_____

_____

_____

_____

_____

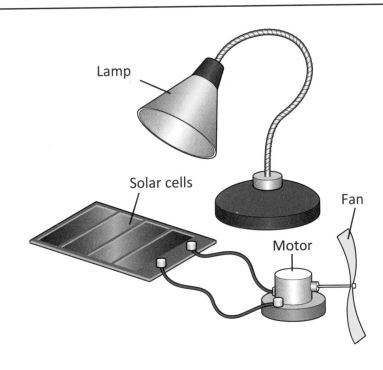

(d) What energy transformations are being illustrated in the image shown above?

_____

_____

_____

_____

_____

(e) Name one difference between a solar cell and a solar panel as illustrated in the images in this question.

_____

_____

_____

_____

_____

(f) In the space below draw and label a diagram of another energy transformation you studied in school.

Question 14

A class carried out a study to investigate the growth of bacteria under different conditions. Bacteria grow as visible colonies on a jelly-like substance called nutrient agar in containers called Petri dishes.

The table below is a summary of the results obtained.

Dish	Set up	Left in a	Result
A	Dish never opened	Warm place	No colonies visible
B	Left open in the laboratory	Warm place	A few colonies
C	Left open in the laboratory	Fridge	No colonies visible
D	Left open in a lunch room	Warm place	Many colonies
E	The nutrient agar was covered in acid and then left open in the lunch room	Warm place	No colonies visible

(a) Which dish acted as the control in this investigation?

_____

(b) What was the effect of the lower temperature on dish **C**?

_____

_____

(c) What does the difference in the results for dishes **B** and **D** tell you about the lunch room?

_____

_____

_____

(d) What do the results tell you about the effect of acid on the growth of bacteria? Relate this conclusion to a named part of the digestive system of a human.

_____

_____

_____

_____

(e) Bacteria growing in milk may cause the milk to turn sour. Suggest why milk stays fresh longer when placed in a fridge.

_____

_____

Question 15

Osteoporosis is the loss of bone density in the human skeleton. Bone loss in space can occur after only one week. When astronauts float around in a spacecraft, they are not using their bones in the same way as they do on Earth.

A 45-year-old astronaut completes a space mission to Mars. Complete the following questions in relation to the graph below:

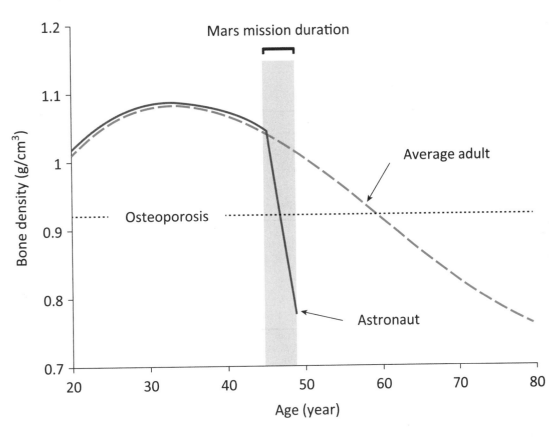

(a) From the graph identify the possible age at which an average adult may get osteoporosis.

_____

_____

(b) From the graph identify the possible age that an average adult on the Mars mission may get osteoporosis.

_____

(c) Identify the force that stimulates our bodies to produce and strengthen our bones on Earth.

_____

(d) An astronaut is going to spend a full year on the International Space Station. The astronaut's current bone density is 1000 mg/cm^2. On Earth the astronaut will lose 1% of bone density per year. On the International Space Station, the astronaut will lose 1% per month. Fill in the table below to show the calculation of bone loss during the year in space.

Month of the year in space	Bone density
Time – preflight January	1000 mg/cm^2
March	
May	
July	
September	
November	

(e) In the space provided below, draw and complete a graph, showing your calculations from the table.

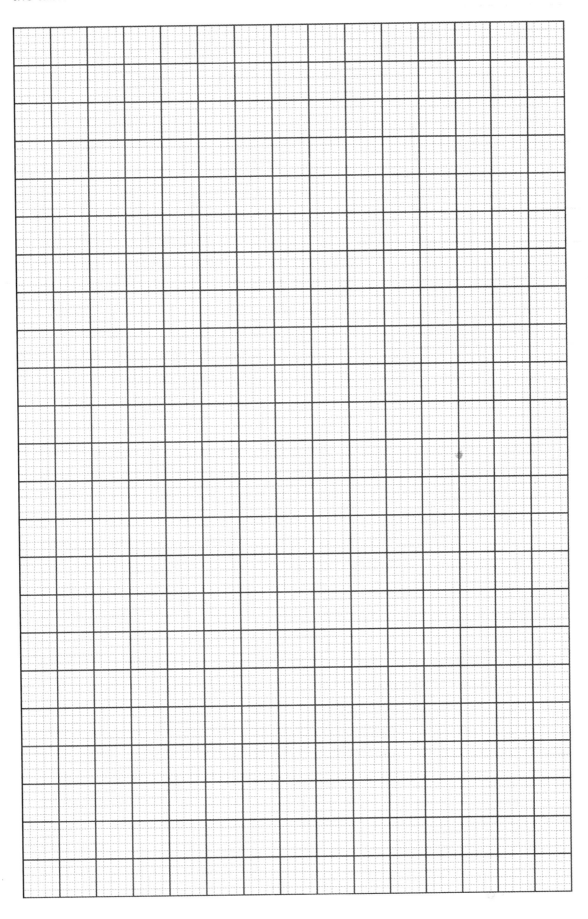

Junior Cycle 20XX
Final Examination
Sample Paper C

Science

Common Level

Time: 2 hours

June – Morning 9:30 to 11:30

360 marks

Examination number				

Instructions

There are two sections in this examination paper.

Section A	150 marks	10 questions
Section B	210 marks	5 questions

Answer **all** parts of **all** questions.

You may ask the superintendent for a copy of the *Formulae and Tables* booklet. You must return it at the end of the examination. You are not allowed to bring your own copy into the examination.

Not all the questions carry equal marks. The number of marks for each question is stated at the top of the question.

You should spend about 50 minutes on Section A and 70 minutes on Section B.

Write your answers in the spaces provided in this booklet. You may lose marks if you do not do so. You are not required to use all of the space provided.

This examination booklet will be scanned and your work will be presented to an examiner on screen. Anything that you write outside of the answer areas may not be seen by the examiner.

You may only use blue or black pen when writing your answers. Do not use pencil.

There is extra space at the end of Section A and at the back of the booklet.
Label any extra work clearly with the question number and part.

Question 1   **15 marks**

Below is a list of a variety of household substances.

Classify the substances shown as acidic, basic or neutral by putting a tick (✓) in the correct column of the table.

One has been completed for you.

Substance	Acidic	Neutral	Basic
Vinegar			
Water		✓	
Washing powder			
Lemon juice			
Toothpaste			
Battery acid			

Question 2   **15 marks**

The diagram shows the human female reproductive system.

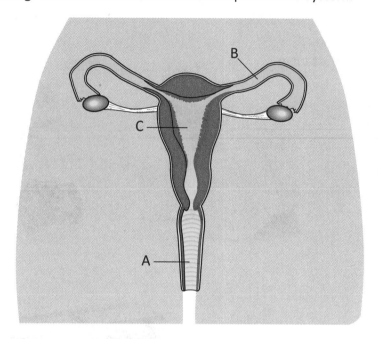

(a)   In the table below write the letter **A**, **B** or **C** opposite the correct name for that part of the female reproductive system.

Letter	Part
	Vagina
	Fallopian tube
	Uterus or womb

(b)   Name the part of the system in which eggs are produced.

_____

(c)   Place a tick (✓) in the correct box to show the day or days on which the lining of the womb builds up in a normal menstrual cycle.

Days 14 to 28   ☐

Day 14   ☐

Days 1 to 5   ☐

Days 5 to 14   ☐

Question 3 15 marks

Answer the following multiple-choice questions by placing a tick (✓) in the correct box.

(a) Identify the force that holds the planets in orbit around the sun.

Magnetic ☐

Compression ☐

Pull ☐

Gravity ☐

Density ☐

(b) Name the galaxy where Earth is located.

Alpha Centauri ☐

Andromeda ☐

Milky Way ☐

Messier ☐

Sunflower ☐

(c) How old is the solar system?

4.8 billion years old ☐

5.1 billion years old ☐

4.2 billion years old ☐

4.6 billion years old ☐

Edco
SAMPLE C

Question 4   **15 marks**

Microscopes are used to view cells.

(a)   Why are microscopes needed to view cells?

_____

_____

The diagram below is of a microscope that we use in the science classroom.

(b)   Name the part of the microscope
labelled **C**, on which the microscope
slide is placed.

_____

(c)   The structure labelled **A** was marked ×10
and structure **B** was marked ×20. How
much bigger did these structures make
the cells appear?

_____

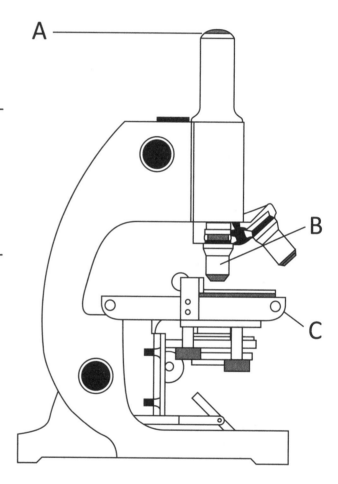

(d)   The picture shows cheek cells, which are typical animal cells. In the box, write the name of
any one part of the cell.

Draw an arrow from the box to the part
of the cell you have named

Question 5

Coal, petrol and butane are the three common fuels used in everyday modern living.

(a) Complete the table below, identifying the state of matter for each fuel.

Fuel	State of matter
Coal	
Petrol	
Butane	

(b) Draw diagrams of these fuels in the boxes below, showing the arrangement of particles in each state of matter.

Coal	Petrol	Butane

(c) State which of these fuels can be compressed.

_____

Question 6   **15 marks**

Pygmy shrews have been in Ireland for a very long time. Animals or plants such as these are said to be native. Pygmy shrews feed on animals that eat dead leaves such as beetles, woodlice and small worms.

The greater white-toothed shrew was first found in Ireland around 2010. Since then this invasive species has spread rapidly across the southern and midland counties. It competes with the pygmy shrew, and in most places where the two types of shrew are found, the pygmy shrew has become extinct. The pygmy shrew is the smallest mammal in Ireland and is about the size of an adult thumb. The greater white-toothed shrew is roughly twice this size.

The danger of the loss of the native shrew is that it may result in a loss of biodiversity. For example, barn owls feed on the greater white-toothed shrew. However, the invasive species does not have the same nutritional value as the pygmy shrew. This is resulting in barn owls producing fewer offspring, which in turn changes the balance of nature in these locations.

(a)   Name the native species of shrew.

_____

(b)   Suggest **one** way the invasive species of shrew may have arrived in Ireland.

_____

_____

(c)   List **two** organisms for which the two types of shrew are competing.

_____

(d)   Explain, naming **two** different types of animals, why the greater white-toothed shrew may reduce biodiversity in Ireland.

_____

_____

_____

_____

Question 7

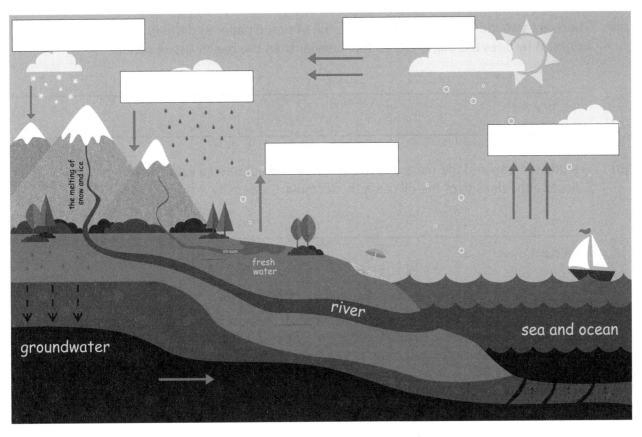

(a) The diagram above illustrates the water cycle. Fill in the spaces on the diagram, using the words below.

Melting   **Evaporation**   **Distillation**   **Condensation**

Decanting   **Precipitation**   **Transpiration**

(b) Explain the following terms:

Precipitation

Evaporation

(a) There are **two** identical school bags, one full of tissue paper and the other full of school books. Why does the bag of books feel heavier than the bag of tissue paper?

_____

_____

(b) A student measured the mass of 200 cm³ of oil and obtained a value of 160 g.
Calculate the density of the oil using the formula: density = $\dfrac{\text{mass}}{\text{volume}}$

Calculation

(c) The rectangular block shown below has a mass of 27,000 kg.

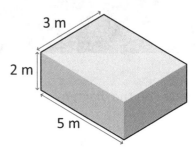

Calculate the density of the block.

Calculation

(d) The density of aluminium is 2.7 g cm⁻³. Calculate the volume of a piece of aluminium of mass 540 g.

Calculation

Question 9   **15 marks**

The myth of 'digital natives'

The ease at which today's tech-savvy students swipe their way through digital devices and social media apps might lead you to believe they know where they are going. But you'd be wrong. When it comes to finding their way safely through the technological maze, many are just as lost as their parents.

Dr Fiona Chambers, acting head of education at UCC who has studied young people's experiences online, says today's digital natives can use the technology, but have "no critical engagement at all". This, she says, leaves students more vulnerable to the influence of fake news and other online risks.

She was part of a research team which recently examined the experiences of more than 600 students online in a mixed, rural secondary school in Ireland. It was one of the first projects of its kind to measure the impact of digital literacy programmes.

It found that more than two-thirds of students knew of someone who had been harmed because of the misuse of technology. Bullying, self-harm and blackmail were just some of the dangers reported.

The Irish Times

(a) What words are used in the above article to describe students who are able to use digital devices well?

_____

(b) What are people who lack "critical engagement" vulnerable to, according to the above article?

_____

_____

(c) "Digital technology does more good than harm." Do you agree or disagree with this statement? Back up your opinion briefly with a supporting example.

_____

_____

_____

_____

Question 10

15 marks

To calculate speed we use the following formula: speed = $\dfrac{\text{distance}}{\text{time}}$

(a)   Fill in the missing word in the following sentence using one of the words below.

mass   **particle**   **direction**   **acceleration**

The velocity of an object tells you the speed at which it is travelling and the

_____ in which it is travelling.

(b)   Calculate the speed of a car that travels 500 metres in 10 seconds.

Calculation

(c)   Calculate the time it takes a car travelling at a speed of 25 m s⁻¹ to travel a distance of 900 m.

Calculation

(d)   Calculate the distance travelled by a person running at 5 m s⁻¹ for 3 hours.

Calculation

Additional writing space for **Section A.**
Label all work clearly with the question number and part.

Question 11 30 marks

The diagram below represents the system used to circulate blood around the body.

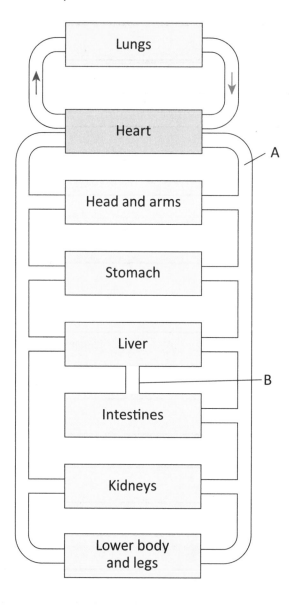

(a) Name the organ used to pump blood around the body.

_____

(b) Arrows are drawn to show the direction of blood flow to and from the lungs. Draw similar arrows on the diagram to show the direction of blood flow at **A** and **B**.

(c) **(i)** Mark with the letter **G** a place on the diagram where the blood gains oxygen.

(ii) Mark with the letter **L** a place on the diagram where the blood loses oxygen.

(iii) Mark with the letter **N** a place on the diagram where the blood gains food.

(d) The body needs both food and oxygen for respiration. Describe what happens during respiration and explain why respiration is important for living things.

_____

_____

_____

_____

_____

(e) Sinead measured her pulse rate before and after exercise. She noticed that it had increased after the exercise.

(i) Name a location in the body where the pulse rate is normally measured.

_____

_____

(ii) Give **one** reason why Sinead's pulse rate increased after the exercise.

_____

_____

(iii) Name **one** lifestyle choice that could cause a person's pulse rate to increase over time.

_____

_____

_____

Question 12   **30 marks**

Feature	Venus	Earth	Mars
Distance from Sun (compared with Earth's distance)	0.7	1	1.5
Diameter (compared with Earth's diameter)	0.95	1	0.53
Gravity (compared with Earth's gravity)	0.9	1	0.4
Time to orbit the Sun	225 days	1 year	Nearly 2 years
Average temperature	462°C	20°C	−20°C
Atmosphere (main constituents)	CO_2, nitrogen, argon, water vapour	Oxygen, nitrogen	CO_2, N_2
Number of moons	0	1	2

From the above data we will compare Earth to Venus and Mars. Earth is given a term of "1". For example, in terms of distance within the solar system, any number below "1" is closer to the sun, any number above "1" is farther away from the sun.

(a)   Comparing the data, which planet has the lowest level of gravity? Justify your answer using information in the box above.

_____

_____

_____

_____

(b)   Give **two** reasons each, for both Mars and Venus, why we could not live on those planets. Justify your answer with data from the box above.

Venus:

1. _____

2. _____

Mars:

1. _____

2. _____

(c) Outline any similarities, from the data, that make Venus similar to Earth.

(d) On which planet would humans have difficulty moving? Justify your answer from the data in the box provided.

Edco
SAMPLE C

Question 13   **45 marks**

When a substance goes from one state of matter (solid, liquid or gas) to another state of matter, the process is called a **change of state**.

(a)   Describe how to investigate the heating of 10 g of ice to observe changes in state. As part of your description, name each piece of equipment you would use (a labelled diagram may help your answer).

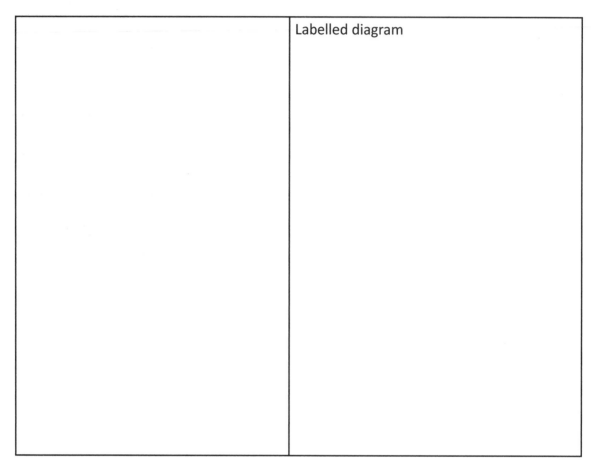

	Labelled diagram

(b)   A heating curve shows the changes as a substance is heated.

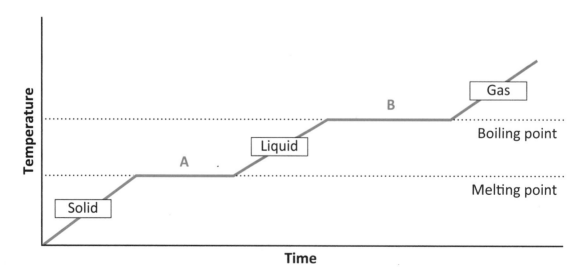

Draw diagrams showing the arrangement of particles in each state of matter.

SOLID	LIQUID	GAS

(c) Name the changes of state at points **A** and **B** on the heating curve on the previous page and explain in terms of particles what happens as the substance is heated.

_____

_____

_____

_____

(d) As ice changes from one state of matter to another, is there a change in mass and a new substance formed? Explain your answer.

_____

_____

_____

_____

_____

Question 14   **45 marks**

A student carried out an activity to investigate the relationship between current and potential difference for a filament bulb. Several different values of potential difference were used. The values of the potential difference and the corresponding values of current were recorded by the student. The data are given in the table below.

Potential difference (V)	Current (A)
1	0.4
2	0.8
3	1.1
4	1.3
5	1.4
6	1.4

(a) Give **one** precaution a student should take in this activity.

_____

_____

(b) In this activity a filament bulb was used. Name any other type of bulb.

_____

_____

(c) The diagram of the experimental arrangement is given below. Label all parts of the diagram.

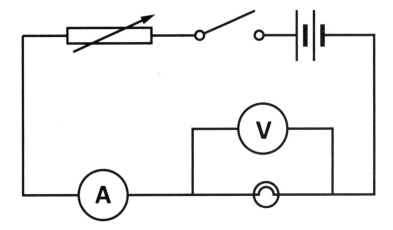

Circuit diagram to show the relationship between current and potential difference.

(d) In the space below, draw a graph of the recorded data.

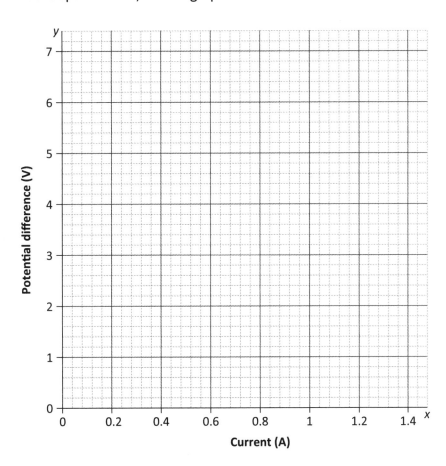

(e) The value of resistance is calculated by dividing the potential difference by the current:

$$resistance = \frac{potential\ difference}{current}$$

Using the data in the table, calculate the resistance for all values of the potential difference. Show your working below.

Calculation

(f) A scientist Georg Ohm discovered that for some electrical components, the value of the resistance stays the same, if the temperature is kept constant.

Would this apply to the filament bulb in this question? Support your answer with a brief explanation.

_____

_____

_____

_____

_____

_____

_____

Question 15   **60 marks**

There are millions of plastic bags in use, and most of them are buried in landfill sites. The number of plastic bags going to landfill could be reduced by:

- reusing

- recycling

- incinerating.

(a)   State the positive and negative environmental impacts on using each of these methods to reduce the number of plastic bags going to landfill.

Waste management	Positive impact on the environment	Negative impact on the environment
Reusing		
Recycling		
Incinerating		

The Earth's supply of metal ores is limited. The extraction of raw materials from the Earth is the start of a product's carbon footprint.

(b)   Explain why extracting copper from land has a major environmental impact.

_____

_____

_____

_____

_____

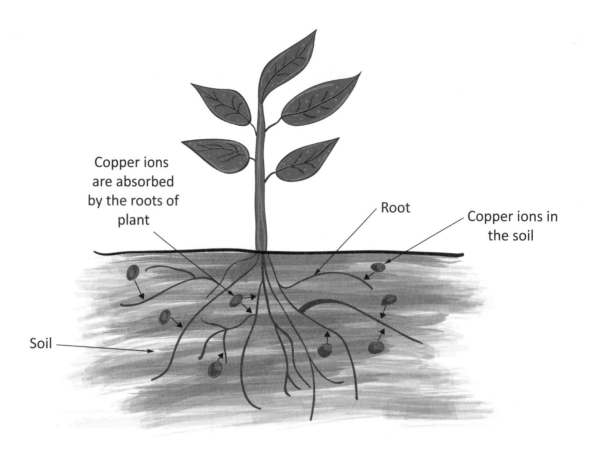

Copper ions are absorbed by the roots of plant

Root

Copper ions in the soil

Soil

A new way to extract copper is by phytomining, in which plants are used to absorb copper compounds through their roots. When the plants are burned, the ash that is produced contains these copper compounds.

(c)   (i)   Give **two** advantages of using phytomining compared to the traditional method.

1. _____

_____

2. _____

_____

(ii)   State **one** disadvantage of phytomining compared to the traditional extraction of copper.

_____

_____

(d) A metal ore is a naturally occurring solid material from which a metal can be extracted. Name the **two** ways of extracting metal from its ores.

1. _____

2. _____

(e) Human activities have damaged the environment. List **four** resources that you think will eventually run out.

1. _____

2. _____

3. _____

4. _____

Additional writing space for **Section B**.
Label all work clearly with the question number and part.

Junior Cycle 20XX
Final Examination
Sample Paper D

Science

Common Level

Time: 2 hours

June – Morning 9:30 to 11:30

360 marks

Examination number

Instructions

There are two sections in this examination paper.

Section A   150 marks   10 questions
Section B   210 marks   5 questions

Answer **all** parts of **all** questions.

You may ask the superintendent for a copy of the *Formulae and Tables* booklet. You must return it at the end of the examination. You are not allowed to bring your own copy into the examination.

Not all the questions carry equal marks. The number of marks for each question is stated at the top of the question.

You should spend about 50 minutes on Section A and 70 minutes on Section B.

Write your answers in the spaces provided in this booklet. You may lose marks if you do not do so. You are not required to use all of the space provided.

This examination booklet will be scanned and your work will be presented to an examiner on screen. Anything that you write outside of the answer areas may not be seen by the examiner.

You may only use blue or black pen when writing your answers. Do not use pencil.

There is extra space at the end of Section A and at the back of the booklet. Label any extra work clearly with the question number and part.

Question 1

15 marks

Material	Density (kg m⁻³)	Density (g cm⁻³)
Polystyrene	20	0.02
Cork	200	0.2
Paraffin oil	800	0.8
Ice	900	0.9
Water	1 000	1
Aluminium	2 700	2.7
Mercury	13 600	13.6
Gold	19 300	19.3
Osmium	22 600	22.6

(a) Name the least dense and the most dense material in the table above.

Least dense: _____

Most dense: _____

(b) Explain why a block of aluminium will not float on water.

_____

_____

_____

_____

(c) Suggest a possible value for the density of the cooking oil in the photograph.

_____

(d) Mercury is a liquid at room temperature. Name one metal from the list above that will float on mercury and one metal that will not float on mercury.

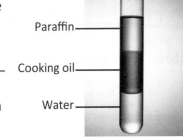

Paraffin

Cooking oil

Water

Edco
SAMPLE D

Will float: _____

Will not float: _____

Question 2   **15 marks**

The graph below illustrates the orbit speed around the Sun of planets within our solar system and their distance from the Sun.

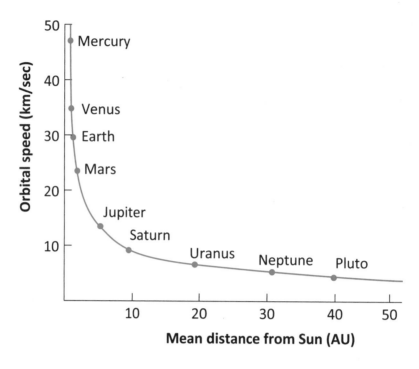

Answer the following questions in relation to the above graph.

(a)   Explain why Mercury has a higher orbit speed around the Sun in comparison to Pluto. Justify your answer from data contained on the graph.

_____

_____

_____

_____

(b)   What evidence from the graph above shows that Venus and Earth have a similar orbit speed?

_____

_____

_____

_____

Question 3   **15 marks**

When viewing microorganisms under a microscope a stain is often used. The cover slip is lowered slowly at an angle.

(a) Give a reason for using a stain.

_____

_____

(b) Explain why the cover slip is lowered at an angle.

_____

_____

(c) Microorganisms can cause disease. Draw one line from each type of microorganism to the disease it causes.

Type of microorganism
Bacterium
Virus
Fungus

Disease
Mumps
Athlete's foot
Tuberculosis

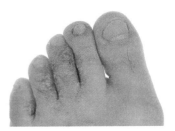

Athlete's foot

Bacteria on a pin

(d) Explain why patients with the flu should not take antibiotics.

_____

_____

(e) Give **one** reason why new medicines have to be tested in clinical trials for many years before they can be used by the general public.

_____

_____

_____

_____

Question 4   **15 marks**

Sound energy can travel fast in air.

To calculate speed we use the following formula: speed = $\dfrac{\text{distance}}{\text{time}}$

(a)   Calculate the speed of sound in air if it travels for 5100 metres in 15 seconds.

Calculation

(b)   During a storm a person sees a flash of lightning and hears the corresponding sound of thunder after 10 seconds. Calculate how far the lightning was from the person by using the value of the speed of sound you obtained in part **(a)**.

_____

_____

_____

Picture A

Picture B

(c)   State the energy conversion that is taking place in the pictures above.

A _____

_____

B _____

_____

Question 5

Substances can change from one state of matter to another.

Answer the following multiple-choice questions **(a)**, **(b)**, **(c)** and **(d)** by putting a tick (✓) in the correct box. Tick one box for each question.

(a)　Solid ⟶ Liquid

Condensation ☐

Evaporation ☐

Freezing ☐

Melting ☐

(b)　Liquid ⟶ Gas

Condensation ☐

Evaporation ☐

Freezing ☐

Melting ☐

(c)　Gas ⟶ Liquid

Condensation ☐

Evaporation ☐

Freezing ☐

Melting ☐

(d)　Liquid ⟶ Solid

Condensation ☐

Evaporation ☐

Freezing ☐

Melting ☐

Edco
SAMPLE D

Question 6   **15 marks**

Metals have different properties, which make them ideal for a large variety of uses in everyday life.

Match the metals from the list **A–G** with the correct descriptions in the table below.

A Magnesium

B Lead

C Potassium

D Mercury

E Aluminium

F Copper

G Silver

Metal	Everyday use of this metal
	This metal is used in thermometers.
	Drinks cans are often made of this metal.
	This metal is a very good conductor of electricity.
	This metal is used in fireworks.
	Jewellery is often made from this metal.

Question 7   **15 marks**

Pollution by non-biodegradable plastics, produced from crude oil, has a significant and damaging effect on our environment.

(a) Give **two** examples of these damaging effects.

1. _____

   _____

2. _____

   _____

(b) Explain the term "non-biodegradable".

_____

_____

_____

A biodegradable cup is shown in the image above. This cup is made from bioplastic, which is made from renewable biological sources such as sugarcane.

(c) Suggest **two** advantages of using bioplastic over the use of plastics made from crude oil.

1. _____

   _____

2. _____

   _____

The greenhouse effect

The greenhouse effect occurs when light energy from the Sun is absorbed by the Earth's surface and heat is radiated back into the atmosphere. Gases present in the atmosphere – known as greenhouse gases – prevent some of the heat energy from radiating off into space. It is this heat that keeps the Earth at a temperature where life can exist.

But what happens if there is a greater concentration of greenhouse gases, such as carbon dioxide, in the atmosphere? More carbon dioxide means more heat is trapped, resulting in our atmosphere getting warmer and warmer. This effect is called the "super greenhouse effect". What was a natural event is now being enhanced to a point where the natural cycles on our planet are being radically affected and may never recover – melting of the polar ice-caps, melting glaciers, rising sea levels, above normal temperatures and violent storms.

We now know that humans have a short time (years) to solve this issue. If we don't we may cause this planet to reach a point where, no matter what we do, it will not be enough as too much damage has already been done.

Now is the time to act and act quickly.

(a)   From the above article, explain the term "greenhouse effect".

_____

_____

_____

(b)   Outline an advantage of the greenhouse effect.

_____

_____

(c)   The article identifies carbon dioxide as a greenhouse gas. Name another greenhouse gas.

_____

_____

Question 9   **15 marks**

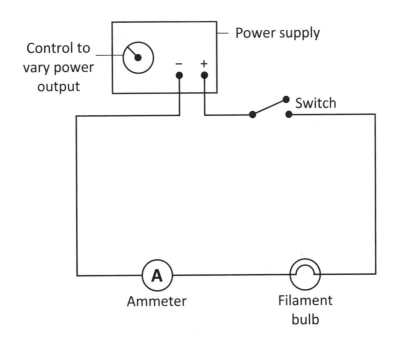

In the above circuit, a student closes the switch, and increases the output from the power supply, by using the control facility of the power supply unit.

(a)   What would you observe by looking at the bulb as the power output is increased?

   Observation: _____

(b)   What would you observe by looking at the ammeter as the power output is decreased?

   Observation: _____

(c)   What would you observe by looking at the ammeter if a 10-watt filament bulb is changed to a 20-watt filament bulb?

   Observation: _____

(d)   As the student continues to increase the output, suddenly the bulb stops emitting light.

   Suggest a reason for this.

   What would be the reading on the ammeter now?

   Reason: _____

   _____

   _____

   Reading on ammeter: _____

Question 10

15 marks

The diagram below shows part of the lung where gas exchange takes place.

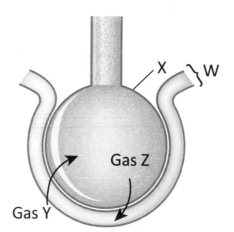

(a) State the names of the structures labelled **X** and **W**.

Label	Name of part
X	
W	

(b) Name the gases labelled **Y** and **Z**.

Label	Name of gas
Y	
Z	

(c) Place a tick (✓) in the box to show which process causes the gases **Y** and **Z** to move in the directions shown.

Respiration ☐

Diffusion ☐

Breathing ☐

Circulation ☐

Additional writing space for **Section A**.
Label all work clearly with the question number and part.

Question 11   **30 marks**

Temperatures of Seasons

The same pond is shown in summer on the left, and in winter on the right. The distance from the Earth to the Sun does not change significantly throughout the seasons. In fact, the Earth is slightly closer to the Sun during the winter.

Summer pond   **Winter pond**

(a)   Explain, in detail, why winter temperatures are cooler than summer temperatures. Refer to the position of the Earth relative to the position of the Sun.

_____

_____

_____

_____

_____

(b)   Describe why winter and summer occur on Earth.

_____

_____

_____

_____

(c) Explain the differences in average temperatures between winter and summer. Use the diagrams below as a reference for your answer.

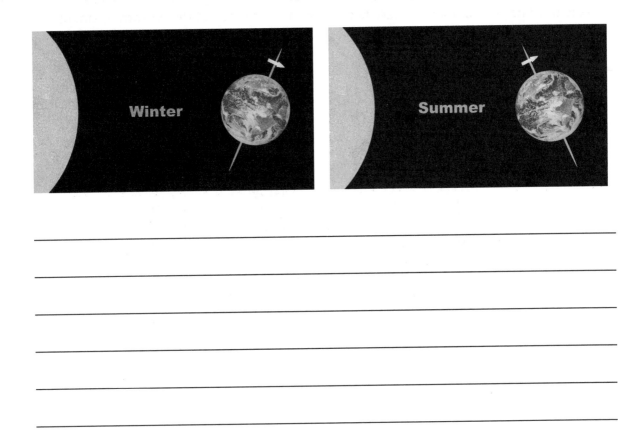

_____

_____

_____

_____

_____

_____

Question 12　　　　　　　　　　　　　　　　　　　　　　　　　　　　**30 marks**

A student is investigating how to measure the volume of an irregular object such as a small stone. Two slightly different approaches were taken. Take a careful look at the two arrangements shown in the diagrams below.

Arrangement 1:

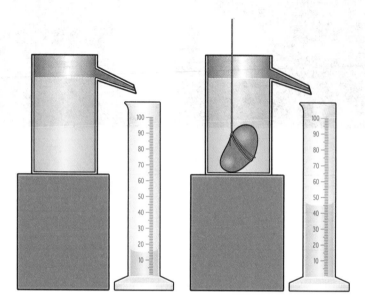

Arrangement 2:

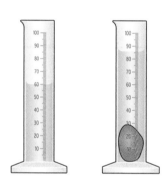

(a)　Name a safety precaution that should be taken when performing either of the activities shown in the diagrams above.

_____

_____

_____

(b)　Give a critical comment on why arrangement 1 is preferable to arrangement 2.

_____

_____

_____

(c) Give a critical comment on why arrangement 2 is preferable to arrangement 1.

_____

_____

_____

(d) Using the diagrams write down the value of the volume of the stone in both arrangements.

Volume in arrangement 1:

Volume in arrangement 2:

(e) A student wanted to perform a similar activity to measure the volume of an irregular piece of wood. However, there is a problem due to the fact that wood floats on water.

Outline in the space below how the student might overcome this problem. Your answer should include a brief written description and a labelled diagram.

_____

_____

_____

_____

Question 13   **30 marks**

Soil pH is a measure of the soil's acidity or alkalinity. The optimal range for most plants is between 5.5 and 7.0.

The table below shows the preferred pH of soil for a selection of plants.

Plant	pH
Apple	5–6.5
Potato	4–6.5
Blackcurrant	6–8
Mint	7–8
Onion	6–7
Strawberry	5–7
Lettuce	6–7

(a) Describe how to test a sample of soil to find its pH. As part of your description, name each piece of equipment you would use (a labelled diagram may help your answer).

	Labelled diagram

(b) List the plants that grow well in acidic soil.

_____

_____

_____

(c) Name the plant that grows well over the largest range of pH values.

_____

_____

(d) If you tested the soil and it was too acidic, explain how you could increase its pH.

_____

_____

_____

Question 14   **45 marks**

The table below gives the amount (in grams per hundred grams) of protein, carbohydrate and fat in five different foods. The energy content per hundred grams of each food is also given.

Food	Protein	Carbohydrate	Fat	Energy kJ/100 g
Baked beans	4.0	17.5	0.4	400
Cooked chicken	26.2	0	1.6	500
Eggs	12.5	0	11.2	600
Bread	9.0	45.0	2.2	1000
Cheese	25.4	0	34.9	1700

(a)   Draw a bar chart, in the grid below, to compare the energy content of 100 g of each type of food shown in the table above.

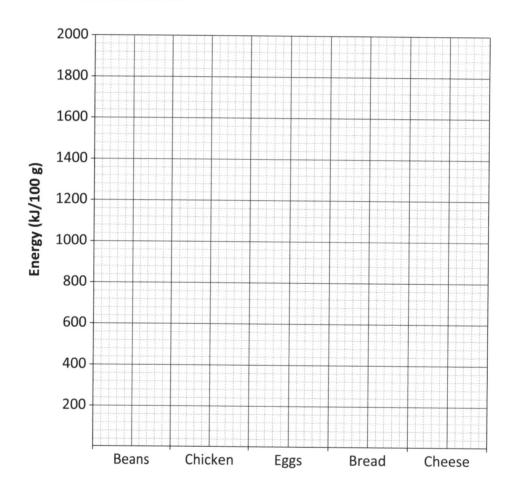

(b)   Approximately how many grams of eggs would a person have to eat to get the protein content of 100 grams of cooked chicken?

_____

_____

(c) How much energy would a person get if they consumed 50 g of each of the five foods listed?

_____

(d) Protein is used to build up muscles. Carbohydrates are mainly used to supply energy. If not used immediately, the energy in carbohydrates is converted to energy in fat, which may block our arteries.

An athlete wants to be strong but does not wish to become fat. Which of the five types of food listed in the table would you advise the athlete to eat? Explain your answer.

_____

_____

_____

(e) Name two parts of the digestive system in which foods are digested.

_____

(f) In which part of the digestive system is food mainly absorbed?

_____

(g) A molecule of glucose is absorbed from our digestive system into our blood.

  (i) To which organ is the glucose carried first?

  _____

  (ii) Name **two** blood vessels the glucose will pass through before it reaches the leg.

  _____

  _____

(h) When it reaches the leg, glucose supplies energy. Name and explain in full the process by which glucose gives us energy.

_____

_____

_____

_____

Question 15

A student carried out an activity to investigate the relationship between current and potential difference for a resistor. Several different values of potential difference were used. The values of the potential difference and the corresponding values of current were recorded by the student. The data are given in the table below.

Potential difference (V)	Current (A)
1	0.2
2	0.4
3	0.6
4	0.8
5	1.0
6	1.2

(a)   Give **one** precaution a student should take in this activity.

_____

_____

_____

(b) Potential difference is often given another name. What is this name?

_____

(c) The diagram of the experimental arrangement is given below. Label all parts of the diagram.

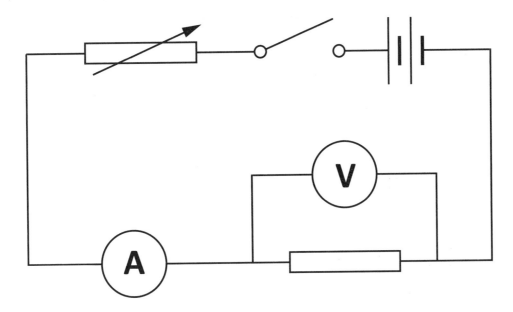

Circuit diagram to show the relationship between current and potential difference.

(d) In the space below, draw a graph of the recorded data.

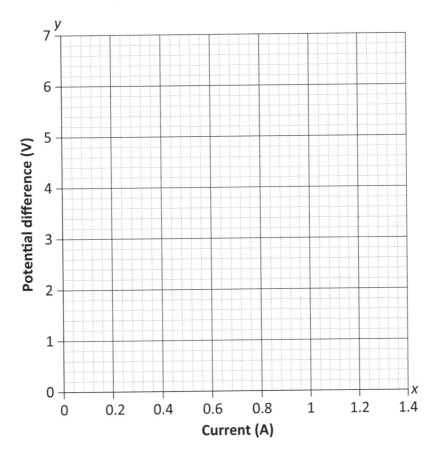

(e) The value of resistance is calculated by dividing the potential difference by the current:

$$resistance = \frac{potential\ difference}{current}$$

Using the data in the table, calculate the resistance for all values of the potential difference. Comment on the answers that you get for the resistance. Show your working below.

Calculation

(f) The temperature of the resistor should be kept constant during the investigation. Suggest a way this could be achieved.

_____

_____

_____

_____

Additional writing space for **Section B**.
Label all work clearly with the question number and part.

Junior Cycle 20XX
Final Examination
Sample Paper E

Science

Common Level

Time: 2 hours

June – Morning 9:30 to 11:30

360 marks

Examination number				

Instructions

There are two sections in this examination paper.

Section A	150 marks	10 questions
Section B	210 marks	6 questions

Answer **all** parts of **all** questions.

You may ask the superintendent for a copy of the *Formulae and Tables* booklet. You must return it at the end of the examination. You are not allowed to bring your own copy into the examination.

Not all the questions carry equal marks. The number of marks for each question is stated at the top of the question.

You should spend about 50 minutes on Section A and 70 minutes on Section B.

Write your answers in the spaces provided in this booklet. You may lose marks if you do not do so. You are not required to use all of the space provided.

This examination booklet will be scanned and your work will be presented to an examiner on screen. Anything that you write outside of the answer areas may not be seen by the examiner.

You may only use blue or black pen when writing your answers. Do not use pencil.

There is extra space at the end of Section A and at the back of the booklet. Label any extra work clearly with the question number and part.

Question 1   **15 marks**

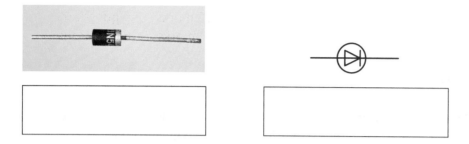

(a)   Which of the images above is the symbol for a diode and which is a photograph of a diode? Write the word "photo" or "symbol" under the appropriate image.

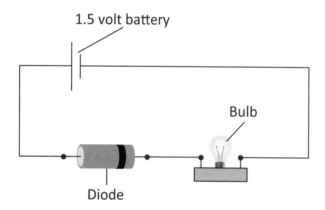

(b)   The bulb is on in the circuit depicted above. Answer the following questions in relation to the circuit.

   (i)   If the diode is removed, there is a break in the circuit. The bulb stays on.
          Tick the box (☐) **True** or **False**.

          True ☐   False ☐

   (ii) The diode is put back in the circuit but is connected in the reverse way. The bulb stays on. Tick the box (☐) **True** or **False**.

          True ☐   False ☐

(c)   Suggest why it would be very unwise to replace the 1.5 V battery with a 12 V battery in the circuit depicted above.

   Suggestion:

   _____

   _____

Question 2

Most human cells, such as cheek cells, contain chromosomes and genes.

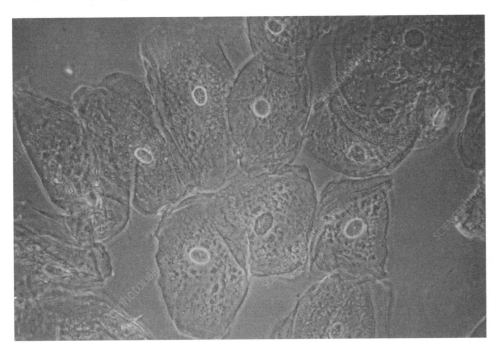

(a) Where in a cheek cell are chromosomes found?

_____

(b) How many chromosomes are in each cheek cell of the human body?

_____

(c) Genes are made of DNA. Name the structures in a human cell on which genes are located.

_____

(d) Some human cells have half the normal number of chromosomes. Name **one** such type of cell.

_____

(e) How many copies of each gene does a person have in each cheek cell?

_____

Question 3

15 marks

Look at the periodic table below.

Select the letters which represent the following?

(a) Two elements in the same group _____

(b) Two elements in the same period _____

(c) An element found in group 2 _____

(d) An element in group 1, period 4 _____

An element that is stable and has a full outer shell _____

MOON PHASES

(a) Fill in the above diagram from the selection of terms below:

Full moon   New moon   Waxing gibbous   Waning gibbous

Waxing crescent   Waning crescent

(b)

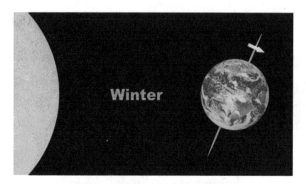

NASA image of winter in the northern hemisphere due to Earth's axial tilt

NASA image of summer in the northern hemisphere due to Earth's axial tilt

The Earth rotates once every 24 hours and is at a tilt of 23.5 degrees.

Use the following words to fill in the blanks. You may use some words more than once.

summer   revolves   axis   hemisphere   towards

winter   rotates   night   away   daylight

As the Earth _____ on its own _____ every 24 hours, the

_____ facing the sun will experience _____, while the

other _____ will experience _____. In addition, the Earth

_____ around the Sun every 365.25 days with an _____

tilt of 23.5 degrees. This allows for the _____ tilting _____

from the Sun to experience _____, while the area of the Earth tilting

_____ the Sun will experience _____.

Question 5   **15 marks**

Elements are made up of one type of atom, whereas a compound is made up of two or more different atoms.

Compete the following table by writing "Element" or "Compound" in the spaces.

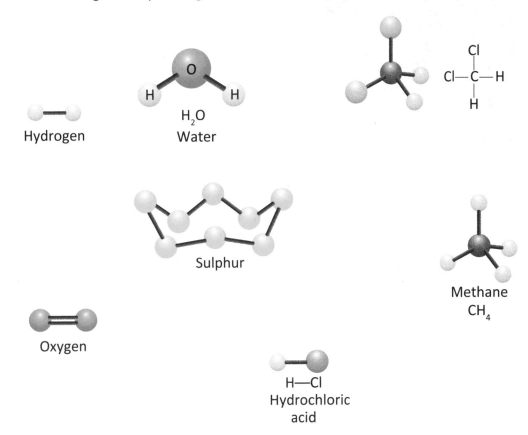

Hydrogen	Element
Oxygen	
Water	Compound
Sulfur	
Hydrochloric acid	
Dichloromethane	
Methane	

Question 6   15 marks

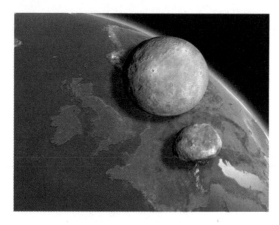

Asteroids are small rocky structures that have no air and no atmosphere. In our solar system they are located in an asteroid belt between Mars and Jupiter. Some asteroids are small and are known as meteors, whereas some are very large and are called planetoids.

(a)   Pluto is now classed as a planetoid and not a planet. Using your knowledge about planets, explain why Pluto was declassified from planet to planetoid status.

_____

_____

_____

_____

_____

_____

(b)   The image above is of two of the largest asteroids known in our solar system, Ceres and Vesta.

Describe four events that may take place if one of these asteroids were to collide with Earth.

1. _____

_____

2. _____

_____

3. _____

_____

4. _____

_____

Question 7   **15 marks**

Leg length in fruit flies is controlled by a single gene. This gene has two versions (called alleles).

Normal length leg is caused by the dominant version "N".

Short leg length is caused by the recessive version "n".

(a)   Which of the following combinations results in short legs?

NN   ☐

Nn   ☐

nn   ☐

(b)   Where in the cells of a fruit fly would you expect to find genes?

Cytoplasm   ☐

Nucleus   ☐

Cell membrane   ☐

(c)   Two fruit flies with normal length legs were crossed. Complete the diagram below to show this cross.

	N	n
N		
n		

(d)   The two fruit flies crossed in the Punnett square above had 400 offspring. How many of these offspring would you expect to have normal length legs?

400   ☐

300   ☐

200   ☐

100   ☐

Question 8

15 marks

A street light, light pole, lamppost, street lamp, light standard, or lamp standard is a raised source of light on the edge of a road or path. When urban electric power distribution became ubiquitous in developed countries in the 20th century, lights for urban streets followed, or sometimes led. Many lamps have light-sensitive photocells that activate automatically when light is or is not needed: dusk, dawn or the onset of dark weather. This function in older lighting systems could have been performed with the aid of a solar dial. Many street light systems are being connected underground instead of wiring from one utility post to another.

(a) In the article above, name the device that automatically switches on the street lights when needed.

_____

(b) Apart from night time, is there any other time when the street lights might turn on automatically?

_____

(c) "It costs a lot of money to light all the streets in Ireland. This is a waste of money."

Do you agree or disagree with this comment? Explain your answer.

_____

_____

_____

_____

Question 9   **15 marks**

The European Union has set targets for all member states to help the environment by the year 2020. In Ireland, 16% of all our energy will have to come from renewable energy sources.

(a)   Identify **four** renewable energy resources in Ireland.

1. _____

2. _____

3. _____

4. _____

(b)   Most of our current energy needs are met by burning fossil fuels.

   (i)   Identify **three** fossil fuels.

     1. _____

     2. _____

     3. _____

   (ii) Explain why fossil fuels are described as non-renewable sources of energy.

     _____

     _____

     _____

(c)   Geothermal energy is heat energy that is harnessed from below the ground.

   (i)   Explain why geothermal energy is described as a renewable source of energy.

     _____

     _____

     _____

   (ii) Outline **one** possible advantage and one possible disadvantage of using geothermal energy to generate electricity.

     Advantage: _____

     Disadvantage: _____

A research scientist was investigating the effects of changing the voltage applied to the heating element in a series of electric toasters. The following data were recorded.

Power rating (watt)	Voltage (volt)	Current (ampere)
500	125	4
750	150	5
900	150	6
1000	200	5
1200	240	5
1500	250	6

(a) Tick the box (✓) **True** or **False** for each of the following statements.

(i) Each time the voltage was increased the current was also increased.

True ☐　　　False ☐

(ii) Each time the voltage was increased the current was decreased.

True ☐　　　False ☐

(iii) The value of the voltage multiplied by the value of the current will give the value of the power rating.

True ☐　　　False ☐

(iv) The value of the voltage divided by the value of the current will give the value of the power rating.

True ☐　　　False ☐

(b) Suggest why the power rating of toasters would be different.

Suggestion:

_____

_____

_____

Additional writing space for **Section A**.
Label all work clearly with the question number and part.

227

Question 11   **30 marks**

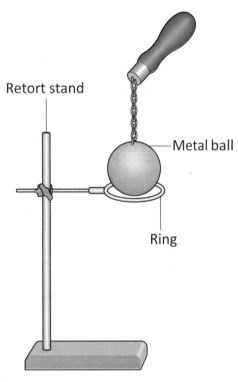

Retort stand

Metal ball

Ring

A student conducted an activity to investigate how the heating and cooling of solids affects their expansion and contraction.

(a) Fill in the missing word at the end of the following two sentences.

Heating a solid will cause it to _____ .

Cooling a solid will cause it to _____ .

(b) Briefly explain how a student might heat the solid depicted in the photo above. Give a precaution that the student would take during the heating of the solid.

Explain: _____

_____

_____

Precaution: _____

_____

_____

_____

(c) When engineers are laying railway tracks or designing metal bridges, they take account of any activity. In the case of either the railway track or the case of the metal bridge, briefly explain what the engineer would do.

_____

_____

_____

(d)

Brass

Normal

Steel

Heated

Cooled

Shown above is a picture of a bimetallic strip, in which a piece of brass has been welded to a piece of steel. Suggest a reason why it curves one way when heated and the other way when cooled.

When heated:

_____

_____

_____

When cooled:

_____

_____

_____

(e) Suggest a practical use for a bimetallic strip.

_____

_____

_____

Question 12   **30 marks**

A group of students made some indicator solutions from three different coloured flower petals. The first step involved crushing and grinding the petals to release their colour into water.

(a)   Name and draw a diagram of the apparatus used to grind up the petals with water.

(b)   The students added their indicators to an acidic solution and an alkaline solution. Their results are shown below.

Colour of indicator in water pH 7	Colour of indicator in acidic solution pH 1	Colour of indicator in alkaline solution pH 12
Yellow	Yellow	Yellow
Red	Red	Green
Purple	Pink	Blue

State the colour of the red petal indicator in nitric acid. Explain your answer.

_____

_____

(c) If the purple petal indicator was placed in a solution of salt and water, would you expect a colour change? Explain your answer.

_____

_____

_____

_____

(d) In your opinion, which flower petal makes the best Indicator? Explain why.

_____

_____

_____

_____

Question 13   **30 marks**

The diagram shown below was set up to investigate the production of energy in respiration. The seeds were soaked in water to allow them to respire.

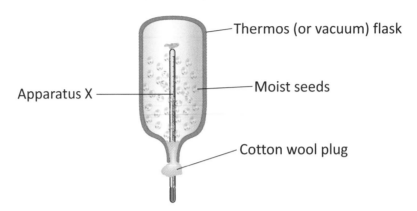

(a) Apparatus **X** was used to measure the temperature. Name apparatus **X**.

_____

(b) What form of energy is being measured in this experiment?

_____

(c) Explain why a thermos flask, rather than a glass container, was used in this investigation.

_____

_____

(d) Suggest a reason why apparatus **X** was pushed high up into the flask.

_____

_____

(e) In a second set-up the same equipment was used but no seeds were placed in the flask. How do you think the temperatures in the two flasks would compare after being set up for 12 hours?

_____

_____

Question 14   **30 marks**

Enzymes are biological catalysts that help reactions to take place at relatively low temperatures. This explains why they are used in biological washing powders.

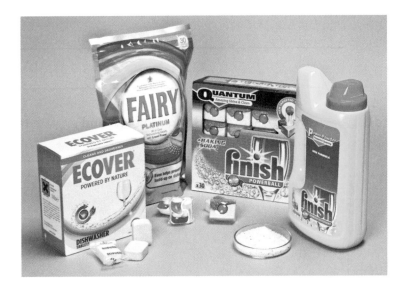

Hydrogen peroxide is a poison that can build up inside living things. An enzyme in the liver can break down this toxin very quickly.

$$\text{hydrogen peroxide} \xrightarrow{\text{enzyme}} \text{water} + \text{oxygen}$$

(a) Describe how this could be demonstrated in the laboratory. As part of your description draw a labelled diagram and name each piece of equipment used.

(b) The gas produced during the reaction is oxygen. Describe a test for this gas.

_____

_____

_____

_____

(c) This reaction will show an increase in temperature. Is this reaction endothermic or exothermic? Explain your answer.

_____

234

_____

(d) Draw an energy profile diagram below and explain how a catalyst can increase the rate of a chemical reaction.

Question 15

A study was carried out to investigate the effects of drinking different volumes of alcohol on reaction times. A small can of beer contains one unit of alcohol. The results are shown in the table below.

Volunteer	Units of alcohol	Reaction time in milliseconds (ms)				
		0.5	1.5	3.0	4.5	6.0
A		34	45	59	71	85
B		35	47	62	75	87
C		32	46	64	72	83
D		30	42	59	70	81
Mean		**33**	**45**	**61**	**72**	

(a) Calculate the mean reaction time of the volunteers after consuming 6.0 units of alcohol.

_____

_____

(b) Which volunteer had the slowest reaction time after consuming 0.5 units of alcohol?

_____

(c) Which volunteer had the fastest reaction time at the end of the investigation?

_____

(d) What do these results suggest about the effect of alcohol on reaction times?

_____

_____

(e) Alcohol is transported around the body in the blood. Which part of the blood carries the alcohol?

_____

Question 16   **45 marks**

NASA have been studying ice core samples, containing dissolved carbon dioxide, for many years. The graph below shows the temperature increase over time due to the increased levels of carbon dioxide in the Earth's atmosphere. According to NASA scientists, there has been a 40% increase in the level of carbon dioxide concentration in the atmosphere since the industrial revolution in the late 1700s.

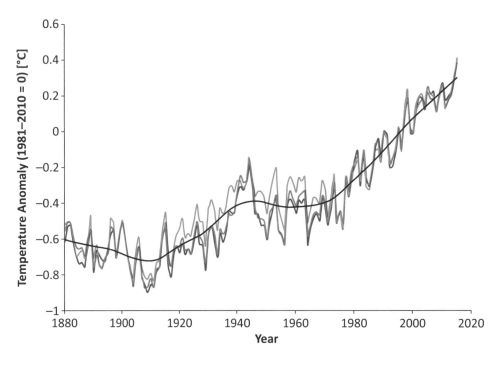

(a)   Using your knowledge of global warming, explain **three** causes that have led to the increase in carbon dioxide concentration.

_____

_____

_____

_____

_____

(b)   Describe the effect this increase in CO_2 concentration has had in relation to Earth's atmospheric temperature level. Refer to the graph in your answer.

_____

_____

_____

_____

(c) Global warming is an increase in the Earth's average surface temperature as a result of increased levels of greenhouse gases.

    (i) Name **three** greenhouse gases.

_____

_____

_____

_____

    (ii) Identify and describe **two** human factors that have resulted in global warming in our environment.

_____

_____

_____

_____

_____

    (iii) Identify any initiatives that have been taken to try to decrease the effects of the factors you have described in part **(ii)** above.

_____

_____

_____

_____

    (iv) Describe **three** pieces of evidence that climate change is really happening.

_____

_____

_____

_____

Additional writing space for **Section B**.
Label all work clearly with the question number and part.

Junior Cycle 20XX
Final Examination
Sample Paper F

Science

Common Level

Time: 2 hours

June – Morning 9:30 to 11:30

360 marks

Examination number				

Instructions

There are two sections in this examination paper.

Section A	150 marks	10 questions
Section B	210 marks	6 questions

Answer **all** parts of **all** questions.

You may ask the superintendent for a copy of the *Formulae and Tables* booklet. You must return it at the end of the examination. You are not allowed to bring your own copy into the examination.

Not all the questions carry equal marks. The number of marks for each question is stated at the top of the question.

You should spend about 50 minutes on Section A and 70 minutes on Section B.

Write your answers in the spaces provided in this booklet. You may lose marks if you do not do so. You are not required to use all of the space provided.

This examination booklet will be scanned and your work will be presented to an examiner on screen. Anything that you write outside of the answer areas may not be seen by the examiner.

You may only use blue or black pen when writing your answers. Do not use pencil.

There is extra space at the end of Section A and at the back of the booklet. Label any extra work clearly with the question number and part.

Question 1
15 marks

Materials can be classified or sorted into different groups.

Classify the following materials in the table below as either natural or synthetic (manufactured) by putting a tick (✓) in the correct part of the table.

Material	Natural	Synthetic
Sand		
Leather		
Nylon		
Cotton		
Polyester		

Astronauts wear orange space suits
for launch and re-entry

Astronauts wear white space suits in space

(a)   From the pictures above can you explain why astronauts have different coloured spacesuits?

_____

_____

_____

_____

(b)   Astronauts have an oxygen supply in their spacesuits. Explain why this is necessary.

_____

_____

_____

Question 3

The atom is made up of smaller particles called **subatomic particles**. These subatomic particles are called protons, neutrons and electrons.

Answer questions **(a)**, **(b)** and **(c)** by putting a tick (✓) in the correct box. Tick one box for each question.

(a) Subatomic particles with a negative charge are located in shells.

Proton ☐

Neutron ☐

Electron ☐

(b) Subatomic particles with a positive charge are located in the nucleus.

Proton ☐

Neutron ☐

Electron ☐

(c) Subatomic particles with no charge are located in the nucleus.

Proton ☐

Neutron ☐

Electron ☐

(d) Fill in the spaces in the following sentence:

An atom with 56 protons and 81 neutrons has an atomic number of _____ and a

mass number of _____.

Question 4 **15 marks**

The male sex cell is called a sperm. The female sex cell is called an egg.

Answer parts **(a)**, **(b)** and **(c)** by putting a tick (✓) in the correct box.

(a)   Where are sperm cells produced?

Sperm ducts   ☐

The penis   ☐

Testes   ☐

The urethra   ☐

(b)   How many eggs does a female normally produce in a single menstrual cycle?

Millions   ☐

One   ☐

Hundreds   ☐

None   ☐

(c)   What name is given to the joining of a sperm and an egg?

Menstruation   ☐

Fertilisation   ☐

Implantation   ☐

Ovulation   ☐

(d)   Name one method of preventing unwanted pregnancies that a sexually active couple may use.

_____

(e)   When a sperm and an egg unite they form a single cell. What name is given to this cell?

_____

Question 5   **15 marks**

To calculate speed, we use the following formula:

To calculate acceleration, we use the following formula:

$$\text{speed} = \frac{\text{distance}}{\text{time}}$$

$$\text{acceleration} = \frac{\text{final speed} - \text{first speed}}{\text{time taken for the change in speed}}$$

(a)   Suggest why a driver of a car will reduce speed when it is raining, and the road is wet.

_____

(b)   Calculate the speed of a car that travels 640 metres in 32 seconds.

Calculation

(c)

Skydivers initially accelerate downwards after they jump out of an aeroplane. After a while they fall at a fixed speed called "terminal velocity". They continue to travel downwards but they are no longer accelerating. They experience a force pushing them upwards.

Suggest what might cause this force.

_____

_____

_____

(d) The first speed of a car is 6 m s⁻¹ and the final speed of a car is 42 m s⁻¹. It took 9 seconds for the speed to change.

Calculate the acceleration of the car.

Calculation

Question 6   **15 marks**

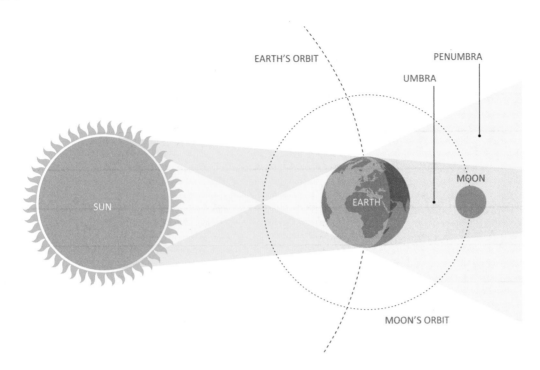

EARTH'S ORBIT

PENUMBRA

UMBRA

MOON

EARTH

SUN

MOON'S ORBIT

The image above shows the relative positions of the Sun, the Earth and the Moon for a lunar eclipse.

(a)   In the space provided below, draw a model of the positions of the Sun, the Earth and the Moon for a solar eclipse.

(b) A lunar eclipse can be seen all over the world at the same time. A solar eclipse can only be seen in certain parts of the world and at different times.

Explain why this is.

_____

_____

_____

_____

_____

_____

_____

Question 7   **15 marks**

This graph shows an energy profile diagram for an exothermic reaction.

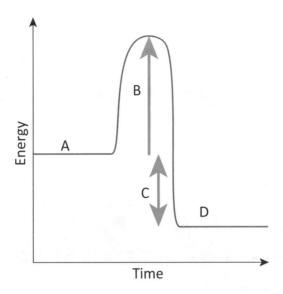

(a) Match **A**, **B**, **C** and **D** with the relevant words in the table below.

NAME	LETTER
Products	
Activation energy	
Reactants	
Heat change	

(b) Did this reaction gain heat or lose heat?

_____

Question 8   **15 marks**

(a)   Draw a circle around the unit from the list below that is used as the unit of energy.

    Watt   **Newton**   **Joule**   **Ampere**   **Kilogram**

(b)   Fill in the missing words using the following list of six different forms of energy.

kinetic energy	**nuclear energy**	**chemical energy**
heat energy	**wind energy**	**electrical energy**

Food is _____ for the human body. Some of the energy that we

get from food enables us to move, which means we have _____ .

We also change some of this energy to _____ , as the human

body needs to maintain a certain temperature. In the winter months many houses are

kept warm using _____ supplied by one of the energy suppliers

in Ireland. The energy suppliers use fossil fuels but they also rely on a renewable source

of energy such as _____ . At the moment in Ireland the energy

suppliers do not use _____ to generate electricity.

Question 9   **15 marks**

Using words from the list below, complete the table, matching the words to the correct statement.

251

| Mercury | Venus | Mars | Jovian | Elliptical |
| Spiral | Satellite | Planetoid | Rocky |

	This planet appears red due to iron oxide on its surface.
	Our solar system has two types of planet: terrestrial and _____.
	Our galaxy, the Milky Way, is this shape.

Question 10   **15 marks**

Cells are the basic building blocks of living things. Match the following statements below to the correct term, by drawing an arrow to the correct term.

The material in cell walls	chromosomes
A thin layer that surrounds cells	mitochondrion
The control centre of the cell	vacuole
Genes are located in these structures	Cell membrane
Structures which supply energy to the cell	nucleus
Contains liquid and supplies strength to the cell	cellulose

Additional writing space for **Section A**.
Label all work clearly with the question number and part.

Question 11   **30 marks**

A student had an infection caused by a disease-causing bacterium. The graph below shows how the number of bacteria changes after the student starts a course of antibiotics.

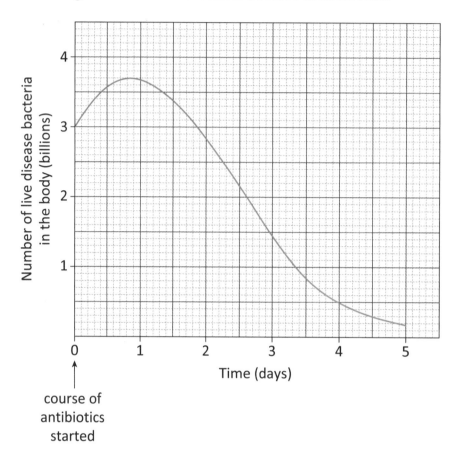

(a) How soon after starting the course of antibiotics did the number of bacteria start to fall?

_____

_____

_____

(b) What evidence is there on the graph that the infection was in fact caused by bacteria?

_____

_____

_____

(c) The student started to feel better on day 3. Calculate the percentage decrease in the number of bacteria between the start of the course of antibiotics and the time the student felt better.

_____

_____

_____

(d) Pathogens are organisms that cause disease. Apart from bacteria, name another type of pathogen.

_____

(e) What type of blood cell helps to control the number of pathogens?

_____

Question 12

There are a number of factors that affect the behaviour of particles in chemical reactions. One of those factors is particle size.

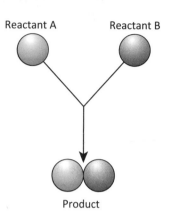

Students reacted three different sized marble chips (calcium carbonate) with hydrochloric acid. They measured the loss in mass caused by carbon dioxide production during the reaction.

Marble chip A	4–6 mm diameter
Marble chip B	6–8 mm diameter
Marble chip C	9–11 mm diameter

(a) Which marble chip has the greatest surface area? Explain your answer.

_____

_____

(b) Draw a fully labelled diagram showing how this investigation was carried out.

(c) How did the students ensure this investigation was a fair test?

_____

_____

The students plotted a graph showing the loss of mass (g) against time.

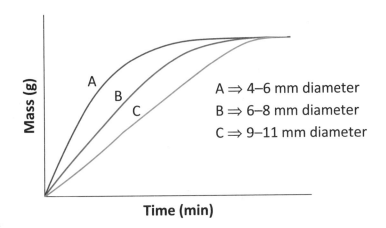

Mass (g)

A ⇒ 4–6 mm diameter
B ⇒ 6–8 mm diameter
C ⇒ 9–11 mm diameter

Time (min)

(d) Looking at the graph above, which marble chip showed the greatest rate of reaction? Explain your answer.

_____

_____

_____

_____

_____

(e) The students then repeated this investigation, adding powdered calcium carbonate to hydrochloric acid. Draw on the graph the curve you would expect from this reaction. Explain why.

_____

_____

_____

_____

Question 13   **30 marks**

The diagram shows a food web from a country field surrounded by hedgerows.

A is a dragonfly

B is a grasshopper

C is a butterfly

D is a house fly

E₁, E₂ and **E₃** are plants.

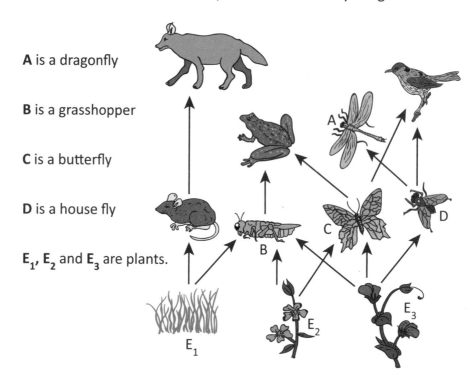

(a)   Write down a food chain from the food web above.

(b)   Name any herbivore shown in the food web.

_____

(c)   Select **one** organism from the food web and give any **one** adaptation of that organism.

Organism:
Adaptation:

(d)   What organism do the dragonfly and the bird compete for?

_____

(e)   Give one example of interdependence shown on the food web.

_____

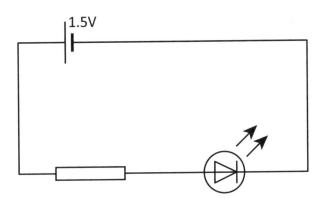

(a)   Draw a circle around the symbol for the LED in the circuit depicted above.

(b)   A red LED is often used in electrical equipment to tell if something is connected to the power supply or not.

    (i)   Give a reason why it is important to know if a piece of equipment is connected to the power supply.

       _____

    (ii) Give a reason why it is better to use an LED instead of a bulb to tell if something is connected to the power supply.

       _____

(c)   The Nobel Prize in Physics was awarded jointly to Isamu Akasaki, Hiroshi Amano and Shuji Nakamura, "for the invention of efficient blue light-emitting diodes, which has enabled bright and energy saving white light sources".
What was it about their invention that so deserved the prize?

_____

_____

_____

Question 15   **45 marks**

Scientists work by making observations, suggesting a hypothesis for the observations, carrying out experiments to test the hypothesis, relating the results of the experiment to the hypothesis.

Answer the following questions based on the nature of science. Place a tick (✓) in one of the boxes in each part of the question.

(a)   What must you find out after collecting data in an experiment?

If the answers are correct ☐

If the results can be corrected ☐

If the results support your hypothesis ☐

If the results can be altered ☐

(b)   Which pieces of apparatus can be used to collect and analyse data?

Scanner, computer, printer, speakers ☐

Scissors, calculator, stapler, ruler ☐

Balance, meter stick, stopwatch, computer ☐

Screwdriver, drill, kettle, clock ☐

(c)   Where should scientists report the results of their experiments?

In newspapers ☐

On the radio or television ☐

In emails to friends ☐

In scientific journals ☐

(d)   Early designers of gliders made wings. These wings did not work. What should the designers do next?

Test the same wings ☐

Design new wings ☐

Stop testing wings ☐

Try to solve a new problem ☐

(e) Which of the following best describes science?

Memorising facts about the natural world ☐

Collecting information about the known world ☐

Reading information about the known world ☐

Gathering information about the ancient world ☐

(f) What should you do at the end of an experiment if the results do not support your hypothesis?

Investigate a different topic ☐

Repeat the experiment many times ☐

Change your hypothesis ☐

Change your apparatus ☐

(g) Which of the following is the most reliable source of information?

A report in a scientific journal ☐

A newspaper column ☐

A blog by a scientist ☐

A documentary on television ☐

(h) When investigating the effect of a new slimming drug on humans, what is the independent variable?

Measuring weight loss ☐

The health of the humans ☐

Mood changes in the humans ☐

The new slimming drug ☐

(i) When investigating the effect of a new slimming drug on humans, what is the dependent variable?

Measuring weight loss ☐

The health of the humans ☐

Mood changes in the humans ☐

The new slimming drug ☐

(j) When investigating the effect of a new slimming drug on humans, why is it necessary to have two sets of humans?

In case some of them get sick ☐

To compare those getting the drug with those not getting the drug ☐

The drug may cause sickness ☐

To allow for people with different diets ☐

(k) When investigating the effect of a new slimming drug on humans, what factors should be kept the same for both sets of people?

The daily dose of medication ☐

The temperature they live in ☐

How much sleep they get ☐

The number of people in each group ☐

Question 16

A student wanted to investigate the relationship between the current flowing through an LED and the potential difference across the LED. The following diagram of an electrical circuit is not fully complete.

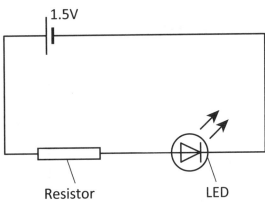

(a) There are four additional components that should be added to the circuit shown above. Name **three** of these components.

1. _____

_____

2. _____

_____

3. _____

_____

(b) In the space below, redraw the diagram to include the correct arrangement of the additional components.

(c) Using the *x*-axis and the *y*-axis below, draw a rough sketch of what the graph would look like. The *y*-axis is current and the *x*-axis is potential difference. There is no need to use graph paper and there is no need to use a scale.

The data recorded are given in the table below.

Potential difference (V)	Current (mA)
0.1	2
0.2	2
0.3	3
0.4	3
0.5	10
0.6	50

Current

Potential difference

(d) What value of current might flow through the LED if a student connected a 6 V battery across it? What might be the consequence of this?

Value: _____

_____

_____

_____

Consequence: _____

_____

_____

_____

(e) Give an example of the use of a LED in an electrical appliance.

_____

_____

Additional writing space for **Section B**.
Label all work clearly with the question number and part.

Junior Cycle 20XX
Final Examination
Sample Paper G

Science

Common Level

Time: 2 hours

June – Morning 9:30 to 11:30

360 marks

Examination number

Instructions

There are two sections in this examination paper.

Section A	150 marks	10 questions
Section B	210 marks	6 questions

Answer **all** parts of **all** questions.

You may ask the superintendent for a copy of the *Formulae and Tables* booklet. You must return it at the end of the examination. You are not allowed to bring your own copy into the examination.

Not all the questions carry equal marks. The number of marks for each question is stated at the top of the question.

You should spend about 50 minutes on Section A and 70 minutes on Section B.

Write your answers in the spaces provided in this booklet. You may lose marks if you do not do so. You are not required to use all of the space provided.

This examination booklet will be scanned and your work will be presented to an examiner on screen. Anything that you write outside of the answer areas may not be seen by the examiner.

You may only use blue or black pen when writing your answers. Do not use pencil.

There is extra space at the end of Section A and at the back of the booklet. Label any extra work clearly with the question number and part.

Question 1   **15 marks**

Read the following article and answer the questions that follow it.

The red squirrel has been native in Ireland for thousands of years. In 1911 six pairs of grey squirrels were introduced to Castle Forbes in County Longford (at a wedding). Since then the invasive grey squirrels have thrived but the number of red squirrels has fallen dramatically.

The grey squirrel threatens the survival of the reds for two reasons: competition for food and disease from greys, which are carriers of the fatal squirrel pox but are immune to it themselves. Other animals that eat the red squirrels include foxes, cats, dogs and pine martens. However, most conservationists agree, the biggest danger comes from invasive grey squirrels, which are almost twice the size of the reds. In recent years it has been suggested that the pine marten, which itself was a threatened species, may be helping the reds by feeding on the greys.

A recent four-year study found a decline in grey squirrel numbers and that the once troubled red squirrel population was able to take back its former range, including woodlands which had been dominated by greys for more than 30 years.

The study seems to confirm that where pine martens had returned to healthy numbers, grey squirrels had all but disappeared. In areas with few or no pine martens, greys persisted.

Red squirrels have coexisted with pine martens throughout much of Europe for tens of thousands of years. The two species evolved together. While pine martens will very occasionally eat red squirrels, they don't seem to have a negative impact on population numbers. In the study, the areas in which reds had recovered in numbers were exclusively those with healthy pine marten populations.

Grey squirrel

Red squirrel

(a) Which type of squirrel was in Ireland in 1900?

_____

(b) Which is the smaller sized squirrel?

_____

(c) Name a resource for which red and grey squirrels compete.

_____

(d) Which type of squirrel is killed by squirrel pox disease?

_____

_____

_____

Pine marten

(e) It is thought that pine martens have restored the balance of nature in favour of the native Irish squirrel. Explain how they might have done this.

_____

_____

_____

Question 2   **15 marks**

Referring to the carbon cycle above, answer the following questions:

(a)   Explain the following terms in relation to the use or release of carbon.

Photosynthesis: _____

Combustion: _____

Respiration: _____

(b)   Identify the type of fuels that are burned and release carbon in the process.

_____

(c) This picture illustrates a "carbon footprint". Explain what you understand this term to mean.

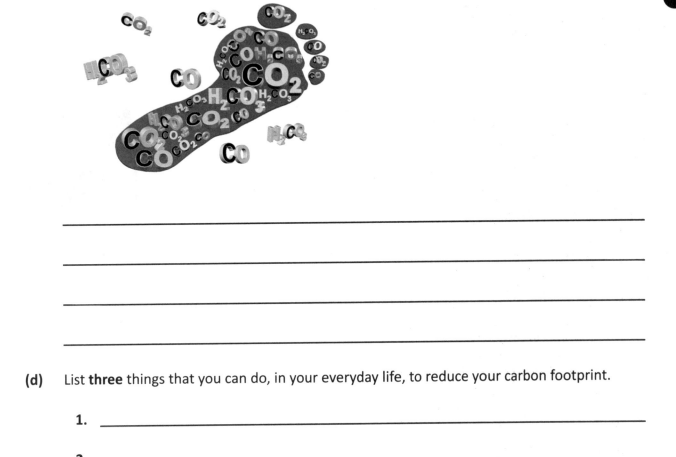

_____

_____

_____

_____

(d) List **three** things that you can do, in your everyday life, to reduce your carbon footprint.

1. _____

2. _____

3. _____

Question 3

To calculate pressure we use the formula: pressure = $\dfrac{\text{force}}{\text{area}}$

(a)   Identify the unit of pressure by drawing a circle around the correct unit in the list below.

Watt   **Ampere**   **Pascal**   **Metre**   **Ohm**

(b)   Explain why the pressure a person wearing stilettos puts on the ground increases if they can balance on the heel of one of the shoes.

_____

_____

_____

(c)   **(i)**   A person has a weight of 500 N. The combined area of the soles and heels of their shoes measures 200 cm². Calculate the pressure they put on the ground when they are standing.

Calculation

(ii)   This person is trying to walk over a deep layer of snow, but it is very difficult as they keep sinking into the snow. Suggest how they might reduce the pressure they put on the snow, making it easier to walk.

_____

_____

_____

Question 4

Bacteria reproduce very quickly. This allows them to evolve rapidly. Some bacteria have evolved to become resistant to antibiotics. For example, MRSA is a bacterium that is resistant to most antibiotics. The graph below shows the change in the number of reported cases of MRSA over 6 years.

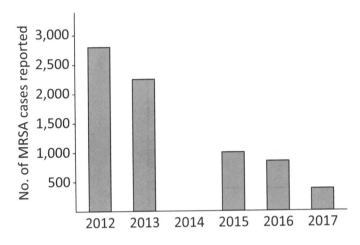

(a) In 2014 there were 1400 cases of MRSA reported. Plot this result on the graph above.

(b) It is thought that improvements in hospital hygiene have resulted in a reduction in MRSA cases. Suggest any **one** such method of hygiene.

_____

_____

(c) Calculate the percentage decrease in MRSA cases between 2012 and 2017. Give your answer to the nearest whole number.

Calculation

(d) Viruses can cause human diseases. Name one human disease caused by a virus.

_____

(e) Explain why doctors are told not to prescribe antibiotics for virus infections.

_____

_____

Question 5   **15 marks**

Using the element symbols below, complete the table and match the different types of atoms with their compounds.

Ca   N   O   Na   Br   C   K

Compound	Atoms present
Sodium bromide	
Potassium carbonate	
Sodium carbonate	
Calcium nitrate	
Potassium oxide	

Question 6   **15 marks**

The rate of a chemical reaction tells us how quickly a chemical reaction takes place. Use the following words to complete the passage.

surface area	temperature	collisions	energy	number

Increasing the rate of a reaction involves increasing the _____ of

successful _____ between particles. For the particles to react they must

collide with enough _____ to break bonds in the molecule. There are four

factors which can change the rate of a reaction: concentration, _____ ,

suitable catalyst and _____ _____ .

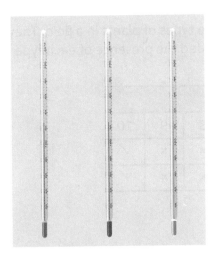

(a) Name a liquid that may be used inside a laboratory thermometer.

_____

(b) Complete the table below by matching the correct words from the following list.

Expansion and contraction   Thermometer   Joule   Degrees Celsius (°C)   Latent heat

	Correct words
The unit of heat energy	
The unit of temperature	
Energy to change ice to water	
To measure the hotness of a body	
The Eiffel Tower in Paris is taller in summer	

Question 8

John and Sarah used a quadrat to estimate the number of two types of plants in a field. They placed the quadrat randomly in ten locations in the field. They recorded the presence of each type of plant in each quadrat. Their results are shown in the table below.

Plant name	Quadrat number									
	1	2	3	4	5	6	7	8	9	10
Clover	✗	✗	✗	✓	✗	✓	✗	✗	✗	✓
Buttercup	✓	✓	✗	✗	✓	✓	✓	✗	✗	✓

(a) What shape is a quadrat?

_____

(b) How might John and Sarah make sure that the quadrat was placed in random locations?

_____

_____

_____

(c) Calculate the percentage frequency of buttercups in the field.

Calculation

(d) If one more quadrat were placed at random in the field, what is the percentage chance that it would contain clover? Explain your answer.

_____

_____

_____

(e) A quadrat is not used to estimate the number of crawling insects such as woodlice. Suggest a reason for this.

_____

_____

_____

Fossil fuels generate electricity by changing energy from one form to another.

Turbine generator

Coiled wire cylinder

Steam entry

Electricity

The following sentences are labelled **A**, **B**, **C**, **D** and **E**.

Turbine blades

(a) Fill in the letters in the boxes below in the correct order to explain how electricity is generated.

Magnetic field

Steam outlet

A   The moving steam has kinetic energy, which turns the blades of a turbine.

B   Coal, oil and gas are stores of chemical energy.

C   The heat boils water to make steam.

D   The turbine spins the magnet near the coil of wire in the generator, which makes the electrical energy.

E   When burned they release energy.

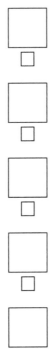

(b) An electrician replaced an old 500-watt outdoor light with a new 40-watt LED light. The new light was as bright as the old light used to be. Suggest a reason why the new 40-watt light gives as much light energy as the old 500-watt light.

_____

_____

_____

Question 10

The picture shows the Hubble Space Telescope orbiting at a height of 569 km above the Earth.

(a)   Explain why the Hubble Space Telescope provides space agencies with more accurate images than telescopes that are used on Earth.

_____

_____

_____

(b)

There have been many technological benefits to everyday life that have resulted from space exploration and space travel. From your knowledge of space exploration, identify two technological benefits and explain their advantage to our everyday living.

1. _____

_____

2. _____

_____

Additional writing space for **Section A**.
Label all work clearly with the question number and part.

Question 11   **30 marks**

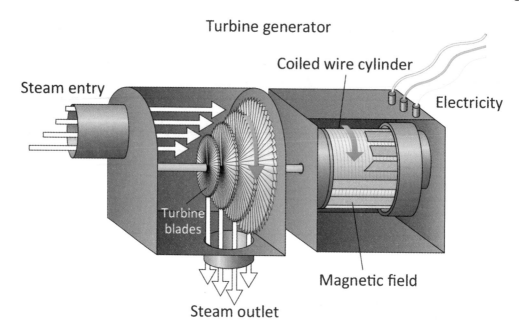

The purpose of the steam in a power station is to move the turbine blades, and this movement can generate electricity.

When a cyclist peddles, the bicycle wheels move and this movement can generate electricity.

(a) How is the steam obtained in a power station?

_____

_____

(b) Is this good or bad for the environment? Justify your answer.

Answer: _____

Justification: _____

_____

_____

(c) Suggest how the idea of motion in nature might be used on a large scale to generate electricity.

_____

_____

_____

_____

_____

"The generation of electricity does not have to involve the changing of kinetic energy to electrical energy. Motion is not always needed to generate electricity."

(d) Give a brief response in support of this statement, including any known examples of generating electricity without involving movement.

_____

_____

_____

_____

(e) Give a brief response disagreeing with this statement as a solution to Ireland's energy needs.

_____

_____

_____

_____

Question 12   30 marks

There are eight planets located within our solar system. Four of these planets are described as terrestrial planets and four are described as jovian planets.

(a)   Explain the terms "terrestrial" and "jovian".

Terrestrial: _____

_____

Jovian: _____

_____

Jupiter   Venus

Radius	69,911 km	6,052 km
Length of day	0d 9h 56m	116d 18h 0m
Distance from Sun	778,500,000 km	108,200,000 km
Mass	1.898×10^{27} kg	4.867E24 kg
Surface area	61,418,738,571 km^2	460,234,317 km^2
Gravity	24.79 m/s^2	8.87 m/s^2
Age	4.5 billion years	4.5 billion years
Orbital period	12 years	225 days
Density	1.33 g/cm^3	5.20 g/cm^3
Orbits	Sun	Sun
Escape velocity	59.5 km/s	10.3 km/s

(b)   From the table above, identify **two** conditions that can be used to classify Jupiter and Venus as planets.

1.   _____

2.   _____

(c) Justify your answer regarding the planetary data you selected from the previous table.

_____

_____

_____

_____

	Earth	Mars
Average distance from the Sun	149,600,000 km	227,940,000 km
Radius	6,378 km	3,397 km
Mass	4.3×10^{24} kg	6.4×10^{23} kg
Rotation period (length of day)	23 hr, 56 min, 4 sec	24 hr, 37 min, 23 sec
Orbital period (length of year)	365 Earth days	687 Earth days
Tilt of axis	23.45°	25.19°
Number of moons	1	2
Gravity	9.81 kg m/s²	3.68 kg m/s²
Average temperature	57°F	−81°F

(d) The table above contains data that compares two planets, Earth and Mars. Using your knowledge of the conditions that are required for life to exist, identify:

(i) Two similarities between Earth and Mars.

1. _____

_____

2. _____

_____

(ii) Three reasons why life may not exist on Mars. Justify your answer using data from the table above.

1. _____

_____

2. _____

_____

3. _____

_____

Approximately 70% of our planet is covered in seawater, which is largely made up of salt and water.

The law of conservation of mass states there is no change in the overall mass when a solid is dissolved in a solvent.

(a) Describe how to show that there is no loss in overall mass when 10 g of salt is added to 100 cm³ of water. As part of your description, name each piece of equipment used and draw a labelled diagram.

(b) Salt dissolves in water to form a solution. Identify the three components below.

Solvent: _____

_____

Solute: _____

_____

Solution: _____

_____

(c) When a solid dissolves in a liquid, two types of particle become completely mixed together. Draw particle diagrams to show the difference in a salt solution and pure water.

Alcohol and water are said to be miscible liquids. Explain why.

_____

_____

_____

The diagram below shows a baby in the uterus, or womb. The placenta and umbilical cord are labelled.

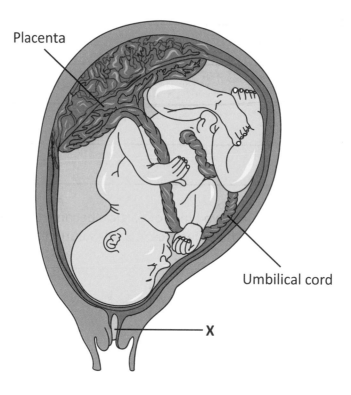

(a) Name the part of the uterus labelled **X**.

_____

(b) The placenta contains blood vessels. Are these belonging to the mother, the baby or both?

_____

_____

(c) The placenta is an organ of exchange.

(i) Name one substance that passes from the mother to the baby. Give **one** use of this material.

Material: _____

Use: _____

_____

(ii) Name **one** substance that passes from the baby to the mother.

_____

(d) It is often said that "a baby is what the mother eats". Do you agree with this statement? Explain your answer.

_____

_____

_____

_____

(e) The lungs of a baby in the uterus do not work. They only begin to work when the baby is born. Explain why this is the case.

_____

_____

_____

(f) The birth of a baby is caused by contractions of the wall of the uterus. Just before the birth it is normal for a liquid to be expelled. What is this liquid?

_____

_____

(g) Babies that are breastfed tend to get fewer infections early in their life. Give **one** reason why this is so.

_____

_____

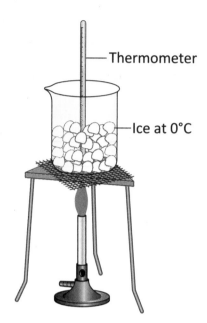

A student conducted an activity that involved heating a beaker of ice at a temperature of 0°C for 12 minutes. The temperature was measured and recorded every 2 minutes.

The following data were recorded.

Time (minute)	Temperature (0°C)
0	0
2	0
4	0
6	0
8	5
10	10
12	15

(a) Name **two** precautions the student should take when working with a Bunsen burner.

Precaution 1: _____

_____

Precaution 2: _____

_____

_____

(b) Using the *x*-axis and the *y*-axis below, draw a rough sketch of what the graph would look like. The *y*-axis is temperature and the *x*-axis is time.

There is no need to use graph paper and there is no need to use a scale.

Temperature

Time

(c) Comment on the shape of the graph that you sketched.

_____

_____

_____

_____

(d) The student concluded from the activity that some of the heat energy was used to change the ice from a solid to a liquid (change of state).

Do you agree or disagree with this conclusion? Justify your answer.

Answer: _____

_____

Justification: _____

_____

_____

(e) The student repeated the activity, but this time the ice was at an initial temperature of −10°C. Fill in the table below with a possible set of temperature readings.

Time (minute)	Temperature (0°C)
0	−10
2	−6
6	
8	
10	
12	

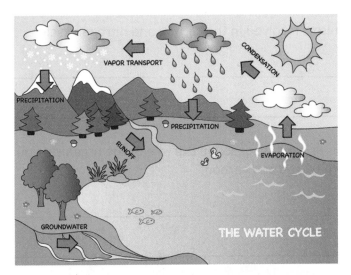

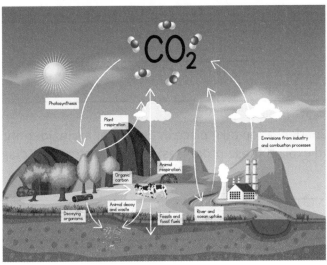

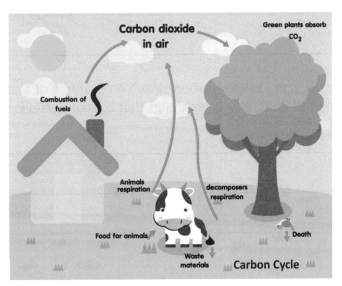

The diagrams above show three cycles that cycle materials within the natural world: the water cycle, the nitrogen cycle and the carbon cycle.

Using the images on the previous page, answer the following questions.

(a) Identify **two** organisms involved in the carbon and nitrogen cycles.

1. _____

2. _____

(b) Using the diagrams as a guide, describe the role of the organism you have selected, in relation to cycling nitrogen and carbon.

_____

_____

_____

_____

_____

(c) Evaporation and Condensation take place in the water cycle. Identify **two** more processes that take place and explain those processes. Use the water cycle diagram as a guide.

1. _____

_____

2. _____

_____

(d) Places that store carbon are called "carbon sinks". An example of a carbon sink is a forest full of trees. Within the trees, identify **three** things that contain carbon.

1. _____

2. _____

3. _____

Additional writing space for **Section B**.
Label all work clearly with the question number and part.

Edco 2023/2024 School Year Planner

FOR FREE ONLINE SOLUTIONS

Day	SEPTEMBER	OCTOBER	NOVEMBER	DECEMBER	JANUARY	FEBRUARY	MARCH	APRIL	MAY	JUNE	JULY	AUGUST
1	Fri	Sun	Wed	Fri	Mon	Thurs	Fri	Mon	Wed	Sat	Mon	Thurs
2	Sat	Mon	Thurs	Sat	Tues	Fri	Sat	Tues	Thurs	Sun	Tues	Fri
3	Sun	Tues	Fri	Sun	Wed	Sat	Sun	Wed	Fri	Mon	Wed	Sat
4	Mon	Wed	Sat	Mon	Thurs	Sun	Mon	Thurs	Sat	Tues	Thurs	Sun
5	Tues	Thurs	Sun	Tues	Fri	Mon	Tues	Fri	Sun	Wed	Fri	Mon
6	Wed	Fri	Mon	Wed	Sat	Tues	Wed	Sat	Mon	Thurs	Sat	Tues
7	Thurs	Sat	Tues	Thurs	Sun	Wed	Thurs	Sun	Tues	Fri	Sun	Wed
8	Fri	Sun	Wed	Fri	Mon	Thurs	Fri	Mon	Wed	Sat	Mon	Thurs
9	Sat	Mon	Thurs	Sat	Tues	Fri	Sat	Tues	Thurs	Sun	Tues	Fri
10	Sun	Tues	Fri	Sun	Wed	Sat	Sun	Wed	Fri	Mon	Wed	Sat
11	Mon	Wed	Sat	Mon	Thurs	Sun	Mon	Thurs	Sat	Tues	Thurs	Sun
12	Tues	Thurs	Sun	Tues	Fri	Mon	Tues	Fri	Sun	Wed	Fri	Mon
13	Wed	Fri	Mon	Wed	Sat	Tues	Wed	Sat	Mon	Thurs	Sat	Tues
14	Thurs	Sat	Tues	Thurs	Sun	Wed	Thurs	Sun	Tues	Fri	Sun	Wed
15	Fri	Sun	Wed	Fri	Mon	Thurs	Fri	Mon	Wed	Sat	Mon	Thurs
16	Sat	Mon	Thurs	Sat	Tues	Fri	Sat	Tues	Thurs	Sun	Tues	Fri
17	Sun	Tues	Fri	Sun	Wed	Sat	Sun	Wed	Fri	Mon	Wed	Sat
18	Mon	Wed	Sat	Mon	Thurs	Sun	Mon	Thurs	Sat	Tues	Thurs	Sun
19	Tues	Thurs	Sun	Tues	Fri	Mon	Tues	Fri	Sun	Wed	Fri	Mon
20	Wed	Fri	Mon	Wed	Sat	Tues	Wed	Sat	Mon	Thurs	Sat	Tues
21	Thurs	Sat	Tues	Thurs	Sun	Wed	Thurs	Sun	Tues	Fri	Sun	Wed
22	Fri	Sun	Wed	Fri	Mon	Thurs	Fri	Mon	Wed	Sat	Mon	Thurs
23	Sat	Mon	Thurs	Sat	Tues	Fri	Sat	Tues	Thurs	Sun	Tues	Fri
24	Sun	Tues	Fri	Sun	Wed	Sat	Sun	Wed	Fri	Mon	Wed	Sat
25	Mon	Wed	Sat	Mon	Thurs	Sun	Mon	Thurs	Sat	Tues	Thurs	Sun
26	Tues	Thurs	Sun	Tues	Fri	Mon	Tues	Fri	Sun	Wed	Fri	Mon
27	Wed	Fri	Mon	Wed	Sat	Tues	Wed	Sat	Mon	Thurs	Sat	Tues
28	Thurs	Sat	Tues	Thurs	Sun	Wed	Thurs	Sun	Tues	Fri	Sun	Wed
29	Fri	Sun	Wed	Fri	Mon	Thurs	Fri	Mon	Wed	Sat	Mon	Thurs
30	Sat	Mon	Thurs	Sat	Tues		Sat	Tues	Thurs	Sun	Tues	Fri
31		Tues		Sun	Wed		Sun		Fri		Wed	Sat

KEY DATES

- ● Public Holidays
- ■ School Holidays
- ◆ Important Dates

2023/2024 School Year Planner

October 2023 mid-term break: All schools will close from Monday 30th October to Friday 3rd November 2023 inclusive.

Christmas 2023: All schools will close on Friday 22nd December 2023, which will be the final day of the school term. All schools will re-open on Monday 8th January 2024.

February 2024 mid-term break: Post-Primary schools will close from Monday 12th February to Friday 16th February 2024 inclusive.

Easter 2024: All schools will close on Friday 22nd March, which will be the final day of the school term. All schools will re-open on Monday 8th April 2024.

5th November – CAO application facility opens for 2024 applications

1st February – Normal closing date for CAO applications

1st May – Closing date for late CAO applications

1st July – Change Your Mind CAO Deadline

The start date for the Junior & Leaving Certificate Examinations 2024 will be Wednesday 7th June.